MEDITERRANEO
EDITIONS

Wild Flowers of Greece

Text - Photographs
Vangelis Papiomitoglou

Translation
Jill Pittinger

Supervision of publication and maps
Mediterraneo Editions

This book is the result of many expeditions into the Greek countryside over the course of the last six years. All of the photographs were taken with regard and respect for nature. Warm thanks are owed to my friends **Zizis Antonopoulos** and **Giannis Kofinas** who provided many stunning photographs for this publication from their extensive archives.

Copyright 2006
MEDITERRANEO EDITIONS
tel. +30 28310 21590
fax: +30 28310 21591
e-mail: info@mediterraneo.gr
www.mediterraneo.gr

ISBN 960-8227-74-7

C O N T E N T S

Wild Flowers
of Greece

Campanula pelviformis

Rhodop

THRA

Orvilos Falakro

MACEDONIA

Tzena

Voras Paiko Pangaio

Thessaloniki

Vermio Holomontas

Grammos Vourinos Pieria

Smolikas Olympos Athos

Oxya Kissavos

P
i
n
d
o
s

Olytsikas THESSALY Pelion

EPIROS

Tymfristos

Panaitoliko

Vardousia Giona EVVIA

STEREA HELLAS Dirfi

Parnassos

IONIAN
ISLANDS

Parnitha

Panachaiko Zireia Athens

Helmos

Mainalo

PELOPONNESE

Parnona

Taygetos

AEGEAN

CYCLAD

Lilium rhodopeum is
a rare lily of exquisite
beauty, endemic to the
Rhodopi mountain
chain.

CRET

Lefka Ori Psiloritis

THE BOTANICAL GEOGRAPHY OF GREECE

Greece constitutes the lower edge of the Balkan Peninsula and is characterized both by its mountainous relief and its multitude of islands.

Its modern form evolved over the last 10 million years with the sinking of some parts of Aegaeis and the uplifting of others as a result of alpine upheavals (orogenesis). The multitude of large mountain massifs formed, together with the position of Greece abutting continents which are completely different in their flora, explains the richness and variety of the Greek flora as well as its high percentage of ende-

Viola scorpiurides is a rare wild pansy which originates from North Africa. Its distribution in Greece is limited only to Crete and Kythera.

mism. The influences of the neighbouring continents have led to its enrichment with a number of species, many of which are only met in Greece out of the whole of Europe. On the other hand, the isolated biotopes in the mountains, as well as on the islands, function as bioreserves with the result that many ancient endemic species have been preserved and new ones created, completely adapted to their environment.

Pulsatilla halerii is endemic to the Balkans and found in Greece only in the mountains near the border with the FYROM and Bulgaria.

Generally, the mountains of Greece divide into two large categories. The first comprises limestone masses which are in reality part of an arc beginning from the Dinaric Alps, passing through the Pindos moun-

Zelkova abelicea. A tree which is endemic to the mountain massifs of Crete. It is the only representative of this Asiatic genus in Europe. Shepherds used to make their crooks from its branches, and since it bore no resemblance to any other known tree in the Cretan mountains they called it 'anégnoro', meaning 'unrecognisable'. The very tiny populations of this unique tree, which has been characterized as threatened, are in need of protection.

'SBOS

HOS

DODECANESE

RHODES

Dikti

tain chain, Agrafa, the Peloponnese, Crete, Karpathos and Rhodes and ending in Asia Minor. These mountains are mainly distinguished by their steep cliffs and gorges, all the result of the slow erosion of the limestone by water.

The second category comprises a series of older mountains which are composed of crystalline schists. These are the mountain chains of Rhodopi, the mountains of Western and Central Macedonia, Paiko, Vorras, Tzena and Vermio, as well as the Thessalian arc dominated by Olympos.

In these massifs a number of ancient plants have survived, such as the three members of the tropical family of Gesneriaceae which are in reality glacial remnants. They are *Haberlea rhodopensis*, endemic to the Rhodopi mountain chain, *Jankaea heldreichii*,

Ramonda serbica

endemic to Olympos, and *Ramonda nathaliae* which in Greece is found on Paiko and on Vorras.

The islands, which constitute that other special characteristic of the Greek area, are also home to many interesting species, even though in a number of them – for example the Cyclades – vegetation is limited to phrygana and scrub.

The islands of the northern Aegean, however, are densely forested, as are the Ionian Islands. The islands of the eastern Aegean are distinguished by their rich flora and particularly by their orchid species. Many of the species found here have an Asiatic origin. Finally, on Crete and Karpathos, which are believed in geographical terms to constitute a separate floral entity, around 2000 species are found of which 10% are endemic.

In its entirety, the Greek flora includes around 6000 species with a rate of endemism that exceeds

Dirfi in Evvia is a densely forested mountain with a very rich flora.

A locality on Karpathos. The incredibly dry islands are home to many rare wild flowers such as the endemic *Campanula carpatha*.

15%. Of the other Mediterranean countries, Italy and Spain for example have more or less the same percentage of endemism but their surface areas are three and four times larger respectively. A comparison with the more northern countries of Europe emphasizes even further the richness of the Greek flora, since countries such as Britain and Germany, which are much larger, are home to around 1600 and 3000 species respectively, with very little endemism. This whole multitude of plants is contained in the many and varied biotopes provided by the polymorphism of the Greek natural landscape. These biotopes are described in general terms below. The series of symbols used corresponds to 5 zones of vegetation which are differentiated on the basis of altitude.

COASTAL BIOTOPES

The coastal flora of Greece does not differ generally from that of the other Mediterranean countries. The brilliant white flowers of the sea daffodil (*Pancratium maritimum*) dominate on the sandy beaches. They are accompanied by plants such as *Euphorbia paralias*, *Medicago marina*, *Otanthus maritimus*, *Eryngium maritimum*, and *Crithmum maritimum*, all with names that betray their maritime preferences. From the fleshy leaves of the latter a pickle is prepared in Greece with the poetic name of 'almyra' ('salty'). The rocks and the sand are also preferred by plants such as *Matthiola tricuspidata*, *Limonium sinuatum*

Pancratium maritimum

The marshes and the brackish waters at the mouths of rivers constitute a biotope for many water-loving plants such as *Iris pseudacorus* and *Aster tripolium* (above).

and *Silene colorata*, one of the many silenes

Phoenix theophrasti

Theophrastus' palm, that beautiful tree which is endemic to Crete and has been classified as 'vulnerable', can grow to a great height and forms clumps in damp, sandy places near the sea. Male and female flowers are found on different trees, and the fruits produced are inedible. The most well-known populations of this palm are at Vai in eastern Crete and at Limni Preveli south of Rethymnon. It resembles *P. dactylifera*, referred to by Theophrastus, but the fruit of the latter are edible.

which is found in Greece. However, the most important plant species of the coastal biotopes is Theophrastus' Palm Tree (*Phoenix theophrasti*), a rare species endemic to Crete which is mainly found at Vai, a place which is under great pressure from tourism. In general, the dozens of islands and the hundreds of kilometres of the indented Greek coastline are a magnet which attracts thousands of visitors, putting a strain on the unprotected seashore ecosystems, especially when rare endemic plants exist. Perhaps the most representative example here is that of a little endemic lily,

Androcymbium rechingeri

Androcymbium rechingeri. The plant has a very narrow distribution at Falasarna and on the tiny island of Elafonisos in south-west Crete. These two places are being choked by visitors, and it is perhaps the fact that this beautiful plant flowers in the depth of winter that has helped it to survive.

The impressive and rare *Centaurea spinosa* grows near the sea along with other wild flowers.

MAN-MADE ENVIRONMENTS

The areas located near settlements, particularly those that are low-lying, are characterized by biotopes strongly influenced by Man. Rare plants are not to be found here. However, a multitude of the more common but no less beautiful flowers of the Greek natural landscape grow on the edges of fields and cultivated areas, on the walls of ruins and on the roadsides. Gladioli (*Gladiolus italicus*), multicoloured anemones, marigolds and poppies abound amongst other plants in the olive groves and fields. The edges of farm tracks are covered in daisies.

Anemone coronaria

The beautiful flowers of the caper (*Capparis spinosa*) and bryony (*Bryonis cretica*) cling to the rocky slopes and walls. The red clusters of common smilax (*Smilax aspersa*) draw the attention, while on the sides of the

Sternbergia lutea at Mystras. The archaeological sites offer themselves for botanical excursions.

hills and edges of fields there are the soaring stems of the giant fennel (*Ferula communis*). Finally orchids, and in particular the impressive *Barlia robertiana* and various species of Ophrys and Serapias, are found in the olive groves.

Gladiolus italicus

A colourful feast of thousands of wild flowers in an abandoned vineyard.

PHRYGANA (GARRIGUE)

The term 'phrygana' was originally used by Theophrastus to describe small, tough-leaved, spiny shrubs. Today, the term is used in a much more general sense and describes degraded, low shrubland on stony, infertile soil. The essential oils, the spines and also the form of the plants which make up phrygana protect them from grazing animals and simultaneously afford protection to a multitude of herbaceous wild flowers, mainly orchids, which grow amongst them. Phlomis (*Phlomis sp.*), spiny broom (*Calicotome villosa*), thorny burnet (*Sarcopoterium spinosum*), summer savory (*Satureja thymbra*), thyme (*Thymus capitatus*), *Genista acanthoclada*, spurge (*Euphorbia acanthothamnos*), French lavender (*Lavandula stoechas*), asphodel (*Asphodelus sp.*), and sage (*Salvia sp.*), as well as the various rock roses (*Cistus sp.*), are the main plants of the phrygana. Especially in the spring and summer, the fragrant aromas here are almost asphyxiating; with the heat, the aromatic oils in all these plants diffuse into the atmosphere.

A natural rock-garden. Many orchids, for example *Orchis italica*, prefer such biotopes.

Such biotopes are to be found from the coastal plain up to the mountain zone.

The rock roses are one of the basic species found in phrygana

MEDITERRANEAN SCRUB (MAQUIS)

These biotopes, which are typical of the Mediterranean, are composed of a number of evergreen bushes which can often take on a tree-like form. Maquis can be the result of degradation by a forest fire or excessive felling of timber from a forest. The degrading of maquis leads to phrygana with the complete desertification of a region as a final result. The most representative species of plants in the maquis are Kermes oak (*Quercus coccifera*), strawberry tree (*Arbutus*

Arbutus unedo

unedo, *Arbutus andrachnae*), myrtle (*Myrtus communis*), ericas (*Erica arborea, Erica manipuliflora*), mastic tree (*Pistacia lentiscus*), turpentine tree (*Pistacia terebinthus*) and sweet bay (*Laurus nobilis*). The vegetation in these scrubland thickets, which extend from the sea to the semi-mountainous zone, is so dense that it is often impassable.

Scrubland with arbutus and heather. On the hill, which has become a place for grazing, phrygana already holds sway.

FORESTS

The Greek forests consist mainly of conifers (pines and firs), and broad-leaved trees (oak, plane, beech). Theoretically, the forest cover of Greece exceeds 45% of its total surface area, but since this figure includes areas which cannot be characterized exclusively as forests it is in reality quite a lot smaller. The forests extend up to an altitude of 1800m, with an exception in the case of *Pinus heldreichii*, a hardened pine which grows up to an altitude of 2400m and is mainly found in the North Pindos and

Greek firs (*Abies cephalonica*) on Parnitha. The mountain is of extreme botanical interest but most people visit it for the casino which is located there.

on Olympos. In general, the conifers constitute the largest portion of the Greek forests. The Aleppo pine (*Pinus halepensis*) thrives at low altitudes, forming

Abies cephalonica

The ancient Greeks called the fir tree 'pítys' after the wood nymph of the same name, whom Voreas cast down into a chasm because she had preferred Pan to him. Gaia felt sorry for the hapless nymph and changed her into a fir tree. Thus, when Voreas (the North wind) blows, the 'Pítys' weeps for Pan and her tears are metamorphosed into resin on the tree. This impressive, pyramid-shaped fir is a wholly Greek tree and forms extensive forests on all the mountains of mainland Greece, especially in Cephalonia from which it takes its name. Particularly in central Greece and the Peloponnese, it is the predominant tree in mountain forests. It was first identified on Aino (Cephalonia), a mountain which is of great botanical interest and was designated a national park in 1962.

little forests from the coastal plain up to 600m. The rock pine (*Pinus brutia*) has a considerable distribution; it is found in Thrace, the islands of the eastern Aegean, on Athos and in Crete, up to an altitude of 1200m. The black pine (*Pinus nigra*) prefers greater altitudes, up to 1800m; it resembles the fir and forms forests mainly on Pindos and in the mountains of Macedonia, although it is also found in the Peloponnese. The truly Greek tree however, is the endemic Greek fir (*Abies cephalonica*)

Quercus macrolepis

which is predominant in the mountains of the Peloponnese and in southern Greece, while in Macedonia it is replaced by one of its hybrids, Abies borisii-regis. In the mixed broad-leaved forests the various types of oak are dominant; the most common of these is Kermes oak (*Quercus coccifera*), the broad-leaved oak (*Quercus pubescens*) and Valonia oak (*Quercus macrolepis*). The beech forms forests in the mountains of northern Greece, while the chestnut is mainly found on the Athos Peninsula. Finally, mention should be made of the forests which, particularly in the White Mountains of Crete, are formed by the horizontally-branched cypress (*Cupressus sem-*

A track on Ayion Oros (Mt. Athos). The Athos peninsula has a particularly rich flora and is one of the most forested areas in Greece.

pervirens var. horizontalis), often in combination with the evergreen maple (*Acer sempervirens*).

Cupressus sempervirens var. horizontalis

The cypress is perhaps the most characteristic of the trees of Crete. It was renowned in antiquity and, as is apparent from a reference to it by Theophrastus, must have existed there in large populations. Despite the fact that *C. sempervirens* var. *horizontalis* constitutes one species along with the lofty-trunked cypress, it differs significantly in its appearance, developing an asymmetrical form and growing horizontally. A particular characteristic is its ability to produce stems from the trunk, which is unusual in conifers. The tree has constantly provided wood from antiquity until recent times. It is said that the famous inverted columns in the Minoan palaces were made from the wood of the Cretan cypress.

above the Greek average, and demonstrates the importance of such biotopes in the conservation of plant wealth. Unique plants such as *Petromarula pinnata, Onosma erectum, Linum arboretum, Lithodora hispidula, Alyssum saxatile, Aethionema saxatile* and also a multitude of fleshy plants (*Sedum sp. and Umbilicus sp.*) are only some of the

The Samaria Gorge. A great number of rare plants, such as *Helichrysum heldreichii* which is endemic to the region, grow on its cliff faces.

GORGES AND ROCKY SLOPES

Gorges and steep rocky slopes are usually a feature of limestone massifs and by their nature constitute places of refuge for many rare and endemic species. Isolation, difficulty of access to them on sheer slopes and the absence of grazing animals have combined to create an ideal environment for these plants. In the Samaria Gorge, for example, more than 400 different species of plants have been recorded, with a degree of endemism of around 20%; this number is considerably

species which prefer such biotopes. A large number of campanulas also find a home on the rocky slopes, among them *C. celsii, C. saxatilis, C. pelviformis,* and *C. versicolor.*

Campanula versicolor

ALPINE BIOTOPES

The effort made to reach alpine altitudes is rewarded by the wealth and uniqueness of the wild flowers that are to be found there. The absence of trees is typical; the plants of the chasms and those too of the thickets offer a feast of pictures in a belated spring, since here the flowering of most of the plants takes place in the summer months. The bushes of Cretan barberry (*Berberis cretica*) or prostrate cherry (*Prunus prostrata*) which tightly hug the rocks, and the rarer, beautiful and fragrant Daphne oleoides are among the larger plants which dominate in the subalpine and alpine zone. There are also typical hemispherical formations such as those

Prunus prostrata

Erigeron glabratus

of *Astragalus angustifolius* and *Acantholimon androsaceum*. The most unique jewels of the alpine zone however are the small, acutely endemic plants which spring up amongst the stones and clefts in the rocks. *Anchusa caespitosa* in the White Mountains and *Campanula oreadum* on Olympos are two of these.

Taygetos. The peaks, and indeed the whole of the mountain, conceal a unique botanical treasure.

THE NAMES OF THE PLANTS

Systematic botany divides the 'Plant Kingdom' into phyla. The plants which are presented here all belong to the angiosperms (ANGIOSPERMAE) with the exception of some conifers, which are gymnosperms (GYMNOSPERMAE). The phyla divide into classes, which in the case of the angiosperms are the monocotyledons or 'monocots' (monokotyledonae) and the dicotyledons or 'dicots' (DIKOTYLEDONAE). In general terms, every class divides into families which in turn divide into genera. Every genus is composed of species related to each other, with the name of each consisting of two components; the first of these identifies the genus and the second, the species. This system of taxonomic classification with its use of double Latin nomenclature was devised by the Swede CARL VON LINNÉ (LINNAEUS, 1707-1778), who revolutionised systematic botany with his work 'SYSTEMA NATURAE'. The Latin names constitute a bridge amongst scientific researchers and use a plethora of Greek words whose etymology - where practicable - accompanies the description of the species in this book.

In the example, the taxonomic structure of two species is clearly shown. The letters which follow the name indicate the botanist who first described the plant. L. refers to LINNAEUS.

THE PLANT KINGDOM

ANGIOSPERMS

DICOTYLEDONS — MONOCOTYLEDONS

FAMILY COMPOSITAE | FAMILY ORCHIDACEAE

GENUS *Anthemis* | GENUS *Ophrys*

SPECIES *chia* | SPECIES *bombyliflora*

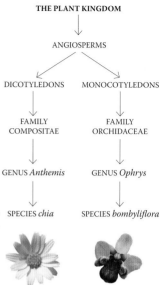

Anthemis chia L.   *Ophrys bombyliflora* Link

EXPLANATION

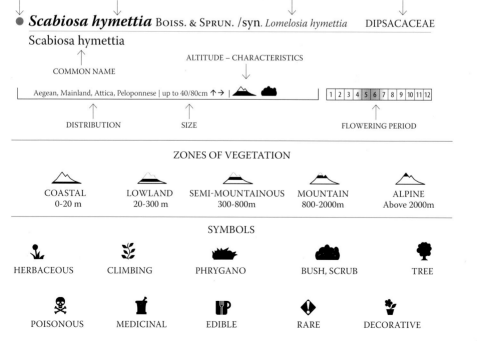

ENDEMIC   SCIENTIFIC NAME   SYNONYM   FAMILY

● ***Scabiosa hymettia*** BOISS. & SPRUN. /syn. *Lomelosia hymettia*   DIPSACACEAE

Scabiosa hymettia

COMMON NAME

ALTITUDE – CHARACTERISTICS

| Aegean, Mainland, Attica, Peloponnese | up to 40/80cm ↑→ | ⛰ ☁ | | 1 2 3 4 5 6 7 8 9 10 11 12 |

DISTRIBUTION   SIZE   FLOWERING PERIOD

ZONES OF VEGETATION

COASTAL
0-20 m

LOWLAND
20-300 m

SEMI-MOUNTAINOUS
300-800m

MOUNTAIN
800-2000m

ALPINE
Above 2000m

SYMBOLS

HERBACEOUS   CLIMBING   PHRYGANO   BUSH, SCRUB   TREE

POISONOUS   MEDICINAL   EDIBLE   RARE   DECORATIVE

DICOTYLEDONS

The dicotyledons (DICOTYLEDONAE) constitute one of the two large classes of angiosperms. As is apparent from their name, they have two seed-leaves. The leaves of the dicotyledons are characterized by a network of veining, in contrast to monocotyledons which have parallel veining.

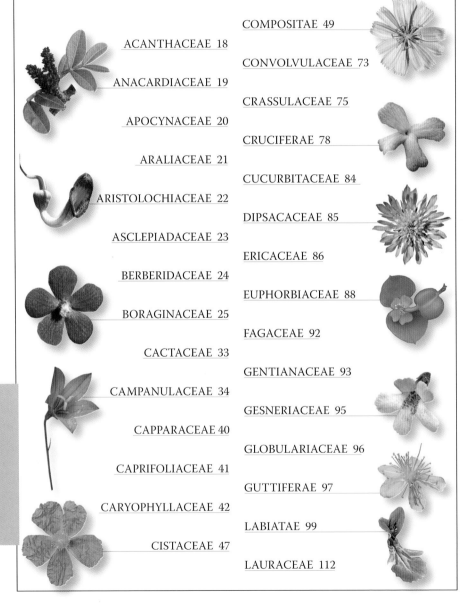

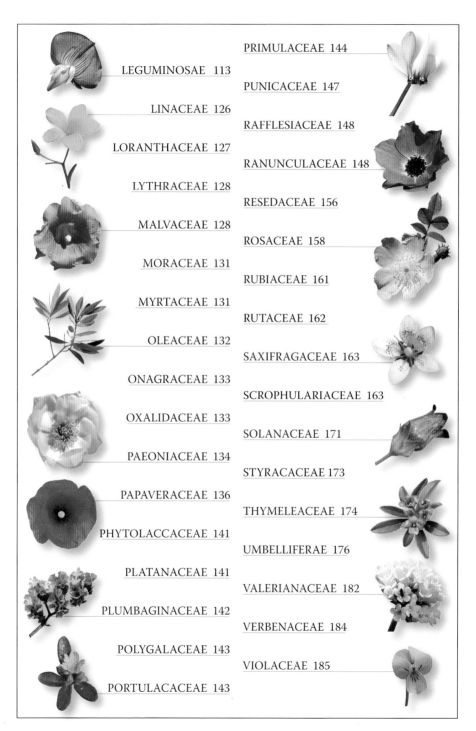

Acanthus mollis L.
Bear's breech

ACANTHACEAE

A perennial plant with a strong stem and large leaves up to 60cm in length, which form a basal rosette. The flowers are arranged in an ear-like spike, white with red veins, covered by thorny bracts. It is a very decorative variety. In folk medicine, the plant is used to treat inflammation. According to Vitruvius, the leaves constituted the prototype for the Corinthian column of Classical Greece, first designed by the sculptor Callimachus. Found in cool, shady locations and very often cultivated in gardens.

The Balkan Acanthus (*Acanthus balcanicus*) which is found in northern Greece is identical with *A. mollis*; however, the lobes of the leaves are narrower at the base.

Thrace, Macedonia, Attica | Up to 120m ↑ |

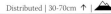

| 1 | 2 | 3 | 4 | 5 | 6 | 7 | 8 | 9 | 10 | 11 | 12 |

Acanthus spinosus L.
Spiny acanthus

ACANTHACEAE

A perennial plant with opposite leaves, deeply divided and with spiny lobes and projecting ribs, concentrated at the base of the plant where they form a dense rosette with a diameter of almost 50cm. The flowers have a white lip, purple calyx, and thorny bracts, and form a dense spike at the top of an erect stem. Common in Greece, it prefers rocky and scrub localities, abandoned fields and olive groves.

Distributed | 30-70cm ↑ |

| 1 | 2 | 3 | 4 | 5 | 6 | 7 | 8 | 9 | 10 | 11 | 12 |

Pistacia lentiscus L.
ANACARDIACEAE
Mastic tree, lentisc

An evergreen, aromatic tree or bush with beautiful green foliage, very common in the Greek countryside. The leaves are composite with 2-5 pairs of elliptical leaflets, smooth on top and fuzzier on the underside. The plant is unisexual, bearing female flowers that are yellow and male flowers which are dark red. The fruits are small and spherical, red at the beginning and black when ripe.

The variety chia (*P. lentiscus* var. *chia)* which thrives only on Chios, is the tree which yields the famous 'mastic'.

Distributed | 1-5m↑ | ⛰ 🌳 🌳 🌿 🏺 | 1 | 2 | 3 | 4 | 5 | 6 | 7 | 8 | 9 | 10 | 11 | 12 |

Pistacia terebinthus L.
ANACARDIACEAE
Turpentine tree

A deciduous bush with composite leaves which are smooth with 2-5 pairs of elliptical leaflets; in contrast to the similar-looking *P. lentiscus*, they have only one leaflet at the tip. The flowers are arranged in clusters on branches of the previous year's growth and the fruits are red, turning to brown when they are ripe. It is from this plant with a strong resinous scent that turpentine is collected, a resin with warming and other properties. The strange 'fruits' which often appear on the twigs are nothing more than galls, the products of small gnat-like insects.

Distributed | 2-5m↑ | ⛰ 🌳 🌳 🌿 🏺 | 1 | 2 | 3 | 4 | 5 | 6 | 7 | 8 | 9 | 10 | 11 | 12 |

Nerium oleander L.

Oleander

An impressive bush, and very decorative, for which reason it is often cultivated in lines along the edges of roads, presenting a unique sight during the flowering period at the beginning of summer. It has lanceolate, sharply-pointed leaves, in whorls of three, and large flowers, pink in colour, which grow in groups at the ends of the stems. Common in stream-beds and gorges. The cultivated varieties may have a white or red flower. The plant is so poisonous that even animals avoid it.

Distributed | Up to 4m. ↑ |

1	2	3	4	5	6	7	8	9	10	11	12

Vinca herbacea W. & K.

Periwinkle

A perennial, trailing, deciduous herbaceous plant. It has smooth leaves, lanceolate and opposite, with a lip slightly turned downwards. The flowers are solitary, consisting of five parts and violet-coloured, with lobes measuring 1-2cm and a tube 1.5cm in length with the stamens enclosed within it. Found in thickets, forests and rocky places.

Distributed | 20-80cm → |

1	2	3	4	5	6	7	8	9	10	11	12

Vinca major L.

Greater periwinkle

A perennial plant, climbing or trailing, with large leaves, smooth and lanceolate, often heart-shaped at the base with a short stalk. The flower is blue-violet in colour, solitary, five-parted and 4-5cm in diameter, with a tube that is hairy on the inside and al long flower-stalk. Found in moist and shady locations. It is cultivated as an ornamental plant.

Distributed | Up to 2m. ↑ → | 🏔 🌿 🪴 🌱

| 1 | 2 | 3 | 4 | 5 | 6 | 7 | 8 | 9 | 10 | 11 | 12 |

ARALIACEAE

Hedera helix L.

Ivy

Ivy was the favourite plant of Dionysos, and in all of the festivals held in his honour it was worn as a garland. This climbing plant with tendrils and beautiful leaves is very decorative and an ideal coverage for fences and walls. The flowers are small and develop in spherical umbels which later yield seeds in the form of small black berries. Found in hedges, amidst ruins and in thickets.

Distributed |Up to 10m. ↑ → | 🏔 🌿 🌱

| 1 | 2 | 3 | 4 | 5 | 6 | 7 | 8 | 9 | 10 | 11 | 12 |

ARISTOLOCHIACEAE

These are perennial herbaceous plants, erect or climbing, with a very characteristic tubular flower in the shape of a saxophone. The latter is very important where the process of pollination is concerned, since the bad smell which the plant exudes attracts flies which go to the tube and are trapped by the hairs at its entrance. During their struggles the flies collect pollen; the following morning, after the hairs have withered, the flies are released and go to other plants to complete the pollination cycle. The name Aristolochia derives from the Greek words *ariston* (meaning 'best') and *lochia* meaning 'birth', because the ancients believed that the plant aided the birth process. About 10 varieties are found in Greece, some of which are cultivated as decorative plants.

Aristolochia cretica LAM.
Cretan Birthwort

ARISTOLOCHIACEAE

This has an erect stem, often branching, with kidney-shaped leaves which are bilobate at the base. The flower is more than 6cm in width, brownish-yellow with a strongly curving tube and yellowish lip with many white hairs. It is endemic to Crete and Karpathos, relatively rare, and prefers rocky, shady places.

A. hirta, which rather resembles *A. cretica*, is endemic to the islands of the eastern Aegean and the beaches of Asia Minor. A very hairy plant with dart-shaped leaves.

Crete, Karpathos | 30-70cm ↑ |

| 1 | 2 | 3 | 4 | 5 | 6 | 7 | 8 | 9 | 10 | 11 | 12 |

Aristolochia rotunda L.
Round-leaved birthwort

ARISTOLOCHIACEAE

Easily recognised by its stalkless, ovate leaves which can have a length of up to 9cm. Its yellowish flower has a straight tube up to 5cm in length with reddish-brown stripes on the inside. The lip has a large, reddish-brown tongue. Found in thickets, hedges and in shady places.

| 1 | 2 | 3 | 4 | 5 | 6 | 7 | 8 | 9 | 10 | 11 | 12 |

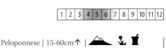
Peloponnese | 15-60cm ↑ |

Aristolochia sempervirens L.

Evergreen birthwort

A climbing plant with very long stems and heart-shaped leaves up to 6cm, smooth on the upper side. The flowers are up to 5cm on a long, thin stalk, brownish-red on the outside surface, and more yellow-ish on the inside with hairs at the mouth and a swollen base. Found in hedges, in thickets and in rocky locations. Very often cultivated as a decorative plant.

A. altissima is similar but has larger leaves, measuring up to 10cm.

Distributed | Up to 5m. ↑ | 🔺 🌿 ❦ ♟

| 1 | 2 | 3 | 4 | 5 | 6 | 7 | 8 | 9 | 10 | 11 | 12 |

ASCLEPIADACEAE

Cionura erecta (L.) GRISEB.

Milkweed

A climbing, herbaceous plant with large, heart-shaped leaves, similar to ivy ac-cording to Dioscurides. White flowers, smooth, five-parted, in umbels. The fruits bear seeds with silky hairs similar to those of *Asclepias fruticosa*. A fragrant but very poisonous plant, hence the popular name - 'death'. Found on steep rocky slopes, in stream-beds and on sandy beaches.

Distributed | Up to 2m. ↑ → | 🔺 🌿 ☠

| 1 | 2 | 3 | 4 | 5 | 6 | 7 | 8 | 9 | 10 | 11 | 12 |

Asclepias fruticosa L. / syn. *Gomphocarpus fruticosus*   ASCLEPIADACEAE
Bristly-fruited silkweed

A tall plant with a much-branched stem and leaves up to 15cm in length, opposite, narrow and lanceolate with a strong central rib. White flowers, five-parted and occuring in umbels. The fruit is an egg-shaped, sharply-pointed capsule with hairy swellings. The seeds inside the capsule have a multitude of silky hairs which were used in the past as down. The plant has a North African origin, and is cultivated for decorative purposes; it is self-seeding in damp localities and road gullies.

Distributed | Up to 2m. ↑ | | 1 | 2 | 3 | 4 | 5 | 6 | 7 | 8 | 9 | 10 | 11 | 12 |

BERBERIDACEAE

Berberis cretica L.   BERBERIDACEAE
Cretan barberry

A deciduous bush, consisting of many branches, bearing straight thorns; the leaves are unlobed and up to 2cm long. The small flowers are yellow and occuring in clusters; the fruits are small, black berries. A plant which prefers rocky localities at higher altitudes, where it sometimes predominates and presents a beautiful picture during the flowering season.

Distributed | 30-100cm ↑ | | 1 | 2 | 3 | 4 | 5 | 6 | 7 | 8 | 9 | 10 | 11 | 12 |

Alkanna tinctoria (L.) Tausch
BORAGINACEAEA

Dyer's alkanet

A perennial, hairy plant with lanceolate leaves. Small flowers, light blue and in clusters. The root was used in the olden days as a dye, yielding a pinkish-red colour – hence the name of the plant. Found in barren and stony locations. Around ten species are found in Greece; some of them are endemic, such as *Alkanna sieberi* which is specifically found in coastal areas of Crete.

Alkanna sieberi

Distributed | 10-30cm ↑→ | △ ▬

1 2 **3** 4 **5** 6 7 8 9 10 11 12

Anchusa

This genus is polymorphic, with hairy plants that are annual or perennial. The flowers are usually blue and more rarely white or pink, with five petals and five little stamens enclosed within the tube. This is a bee-keeper's plant and its roots contain a red pigment. About seven varieties grow in Greece.

Anchusa azurea Mill. / syn. *Anchusa italica*
BORAGINACEAE

Large blue alkanet

The tallest of the anchusae, this is a beautiful plant with a densely branching, hairy stem. The leaves are lanceolate and entire; the lower leaves are large and stalked, the upper leaves are smaller and stalkless. The calyx has pointed tips and the flowers are blue or violet in colour, of a light shade in the centre and arranged in groups at the ends of the stems. Very common on roadsides and in abandoned fields.

A. aegyptiaca is a small annual with a cream-coloured flower; it prefers coastal locations. In Greece it is found in eastern Crete and in the south-east Aegean.

Anchusa aegyptiaca

Crete | 50-120cm ↑ | △ ⚘

1 2 3 **4** 5 **6** 7 8 9 10 11 12

Anchusa cespitosa Lam.

BORAGINACEAE

Anchusa cespitosa

A plant with very short stems and elongated leaves, hairy and arranged in small rosettes. Endemic to the White Mountains of Crete, it is perhaps the most beautiful of the Greek ravine plants. The plant, which develops on the rocks and covers them with the dazzling blue of its flowers, makes an impressive picture and it is not by chance that shepherds name it for its colour – *blávi*, meaning 'blue'.

Crete (The White Mountains) | Up to 50cm ↑ | 　　　　　　　 | 1 2 3 4 5 6 7 8 9 10 11 12

Anchusa undulata Lam. / syn. *Anchusa hybrida*

BORAGINACEAE

Undulate anchusa

An annual, hairy plant with leaves concentrated at the base, large, lanceolate and with an undulating lip, giving the plant its name. Up to 5 flowers at the tips of the stems, small and funnel-like, blue or pink with sharply pointed petals. Found in fields, on slopes and roadsides.

Distributed | 20-40cm ↑ | 　　　　　 | 1 2 3 4 5 6 7 8 9 10 11 12

Anchusa variegata LEHM.

Variegated anchusa

As is apparent from its name, *A. variegata* is a plant with flowers that are a variety of colours. They are small and tubular, with five small, unequal white petals, with pink, violet or light blue spots. The calyx has five sharply-pointed lobes. A perennial, rather procumbent plant with leaves that have white stippling and are lanceolate, toothed, and bristly at the lip. Found in rocky locations, on slopes, and in ditches, often near the sea.

Distributed | 10-30cm →

| 1 | 2 | 3 | 4 | 5 | 6 | 7 | 8 | 9 | 10 | 11 | 12 |

Borago officinalis L.

Borage

This is an annual plant, rich in potassium and other nitrous salts which give it a number of medicinal uses. It has a much-branching habit, and is hairy with large, stalked leaves that are ovate at the base; the upper ones are smaller and stalkless. Star-shaped flowers on long stalks, 'nodding' and blue in colour, and calyces with five narrow, lanceolate sepals which are shorter than the petals. Found in cultivated and fallow fields, phrygana etc.

Distributed | More than 70cm ↑

| 1 | 2 | 3 | 4 | 5 | 6 | 7 | 8 | 9 | 10 | 11 | 12 |

Cynoglossum columnae TEN.   BORAGINACEAE
Houndstongue

An annual with large leaves, downy and stalked, the upper leaves stalkless. Small flowers, cup-shaped and brownish-red with five petals, covered by downy sepals of equal length. The name derives from the Greek words for 'dog' and 'tongue', and refers to the shape of the leaves. Found on the edges of fields, on slopes, and in stony locations.

Distributed | 25-45cm ↑ | ▲ ⚓ | 1 | 2 | 3 | 4 | 5 | 6 | 7 | 8 | 9 | 10 | 11 | 12 |

Cynoglossum creticum MILL.   BORAGINACEAE
Cretan houndstongue, Blue houndstongue

Similar to *C. columnae*, but with beautiful flowers of up to 12 mm, pinkish-red or light blue at maturity, with darker veining in the same colours. The thorny fruits were at one time a favourite plaything with children, since they adhere easily to clothing. Found in rocky locations, olive groves and on the edges of fields.

Distributed | 20-60cm ↑ | ▲ ⚓ | 1 | 2 | 3 | 4 | 5 | 6 | 7 | 8 | 9 | 10 | 11 | 12 |

Echium italicum L.

Pale bugloss

The name of this genus derives from the Greek word for 'viper' and refers to the shape of the fruit which resembles that of the head of the snake. *E. italicum* is a biennial, hairy, with a central stem which has many branches and gives it a very characteristic pyramidal shape. The leaves at the base are large, lanceolate, and concentrated in a rosette. The flowers are zygomorphic, in gentle shades of red and light blue, with the stamens projecting quite a way out of the corolla. Found in dry locations, uncultivated fields and on roadsides.

Distributed | 30-100cm ↑ |

| 1 | 2 | 3 | 4 | 5 | 6 | 7 | 8 | 9 | 10 | 11 | 12 |

Echium plantagineum L.

Purple viper's bugloss

A biennial plant, slightly downy. The leaves at the base are large with strong veining, in a rosette. A zygomorphic flower, red in colour at first and then gradually becoming mauve-blue. The calyx is short. Easily identified by its two protruding stamens. Normally found near the sea.

Distributed | 20-70cm ↑ |

| 1 | 2 | 3 | 4 | 5 | 6 | 7 | 8 | 9 | 10 | 11 | 12 |

Echium angustifolium Mill.

BORAGINACEAE

Narrow-leaved bugloss

A hairy plant, much-branching and with narrow lanceolate leaves, from which it takes its name. The flower is usually purple or red with four projecting stamens. Found in rocky locations, on slopes, and often near the sea.

Crete, Aegean | 25-40cm ↑ | 〰️ 🌿 ⚘ | 1 | 2 | 3 | 4 | 5 | 6 | 7 | 8 | 9 | 10 | 11 | 12 |

Heliotropium europaeum L.

BORAGINACEAE

Heliotrope

A plant which is distinctive because of its curled, spiral flower-spikes. It has ovate leaves, lanceolate and downy, stalked and with marked veining, and white flowers with five petals which bloom from the bottom of the spike to the tip, the spiral of flowers opening slowly. The name comes from the Greek word for 'sun' and the verb meaning 'to change direction', since it is believed that the flowers turn towards the sun. Found in olive groves, uncultivated fields, and on roadsides.

Other varieties of *Heliotropium* grow in Greece; they resemble the latter, and some of them are aromatic.

Crete | 5-40cm → ↑ | 〰️ ⚘ | 1 | 2 | 3 | 4 | 5 | 6 | 7 | 8 | 9 | 10 | 11 | 12 |

Lithodora hispidula (Sm.) Griseb.

Lithodora hispidula

A multi-stemmed phrygano plant, woody at the base with small, lanceolate, leathery leaves, with coarse hairs. Small flowers, five-lobed, bell-shaped, light blue or violet with a short, hairy calyx. It often grows amongst stones, a habit which gives its name from the Greek words for 'stone' and 'gift'. Found in ravines, rocky locations, and on vertical slopes.

Crete, Aegean, Rhodes | 10-40cm ↑ | ▲▲ 🌿 ◆

| 1 | 2 | 3 | 4 | 5 | 6 | 7 | 8 | 9 | 10 | 11 | 12 |

Onosma

Beautiful phrygana plants, very hairy with characteristic tubular flowers, normally yellow and more rarely white. They are quite difficult to identify, since all the varieties have more or less the same characteristics. Around 15 species are found in Greece, some of which are endemic with a limited distribution. The name derives from the Greek words for 'donkey' and 'scent', recalling the way that donkeys seek out the plant.

Onosma erectum Sm.

Onosma erectum

A very beautiful perennial, with numerous erect stems and lanceolate, hairy leaves which are narrower. Yellow flowers, tubular and up to 4cm long, in dense, nodding tresses, with a sharply-lobed calyx which extends up to the middle of the tube. Found usually on slopes and in stony locations.

Sterea, Peloponnese, Crete, Aegean | 10-60cm ↑→ | ▲▲ 🌿 ◆

| 1 | 2 | 3 | 4 | 5 | 6 | 7 | 8 | 9 | 10 | 11 | 12 |

Onosma frutescens Lam.

BORAGINACEAE

Golden drop

A perennial phrygano plant, much-branched, with dense white hairs, russet-coloured stems and lanceolate leaves which are narrower at the base. The flowers are almost cylindrical and arranged in nodding tresses, yellow, russet on the lip and with a calyx that has russet-coloured, sharply-pointed lobes to 2/3 of the corolla. Found in rocky places.

Sterea, Aegean, Peloponnese | 20-50cm ↑ | 1 2 3 **4 5 6 7** 8 9 10 11 12

Onosma graecum Boiss.

BORAGINACEAE

Onosma graecum

A biennial phrygano plant, very hairy. The rosette of oblong leaves develops during the first year, while in the second year the stem develops with lanceolate leaves. The flowers of up to 2cm are in a cone-shaped cluster, tubular, yellow, and russet at maturity with a calyx to 2/3 of the tube. Found in dry, stony locations.

Crete, Aegean, Peloponnese | Up to 40cm ↑ | 1 2 3 **4 5 6 7** 8 9 10 11 12

Procopiania cretica (Willd) Gusul. / syn. *Symphytum creticum*   BORAGINACEAE
Procopiana

A plant with rough hairs and large, dart-like leaves, heart-shaped with clear veining. The flower is very characteristic with five petals that are white, or more rarely light blue, long and thin, and turned backwards. The calyx has pointed lobes the length of the tube. Found on shady, rocky slopes.

Crete, Karpathos, Peloponnese, Ionian Is. | Up to 50cm ↑ | ▲ ⬓ ◆ | 1 2 3 4 5 6 7 8 9 10 11 12

CACTACEAE

Opuntia ficus-indica Mill.   CACTACEAE
Prickly pear

Although a native of America, the prickly pear has acclimatized itself so well that it thrives in all the countries of the Mediterranean. It can take the form of a tree, although it more commonly occurs as a bush along hedgerows or fences. The stems consist of jointed, oval, fleshy segments, very prickly, and their length can reach to 40cm. The flowers are yellow. The fruit is cylindrical, red with countless tiny spines; it is very tasty and enjoyed during the Greek summer by those who 'know how to prepare them'.

Distributed | Up to 5m ↑ | ▲ ⬛ ♣ ℍℙ ⚘ | 1 2 3 4 5 6 7 8 9 10 11 12

CAMPANULACEAE

Campanula

The campanulas were thus named because their flowers exactly resemble little bells. They are five-lobed, nearly always light blue or violet in colour and only rarely white. This is a large genus, represented in Greece by more than 70 species and subspecies of which quite a number are endemic, usually with a very small distribution. The campanulas are very decorative plants and are very often to be seen under cultivation in gardens.

• *Campanula aizoon* Boiss. & Heldr.

CAMPANULACEAE

Campanula aizoon

One of the rarer campanulas with a restricted distribution on Parnassos, Gion, Helmo and in the White Mountains of Crete. It has a strong stem with a height often up to 30cm; the leaves are at the base, arranged in a rosette. The flowers are small, up to 1.5cm, dark bluish-violet, and the calyx has pointed lobes. It grows in rocky locations with a very small distribution and has been characterized as 'vulnerable'. The name comes from the Greek meaning 'that which lives forever'.

Peloponnese, Crete, Sterea | 10-40cm ↑ | ⛰ ⚘ ◆ | 1 2 3 4 5 6 7 8 9 10 11 12

• *Campanula celsii* ssp.*celsii* A. DC.

CAMPANULACEAE

Campanula celsii

A biennial with a much-branched, downy stem. The leaves at the base have irregular lobes, while the upper leaves are ovate, toothed, and stalkless. The flowers are tubular and dark blue, up to 3cm long, and the calyx has little ears between the sharply pointed lobes. Found in rocky places in the mountains of Attica.

Attica | Up to 50cm → | ⛰ ⚘ ◆ | 1 2 3 4 5 6 7 8 9 10 11 12

Campanula drabifolia Sibth.& Sm.

Campanula drabifolia

A dwarf plant, hairy with elliptical leaves which are toothed
and narrow at the base. Small
flowers of up to 1cm,
bluish-violet with a
white tube. Found in
rocky places. This little
campanula is met nearly
everywhere in Greece except
for Crete, where it is replaced by
the similar-looking *C. erinus*.

Distributed | 10-20cm ↑ |

| 1 | 2 | 3 | 4 | 5 | 6 | 7 | 8 | 9 | 10 | 11 | 12 |

• *Campanula oreadum* Boiss. & Heldr.

Campanula oreadum

This beautiful, small campanula is a rare endemic
plant on Olympus. Its stem does not exceed 15cm
in height. It grows inside clefts in the rocks at alpine
altitudes and flowers late in the summer. The name
refers to the Oreiades – the nymphs of the mountains in Greek mythology (*óros* = mountain).

Thessaly (Olympos) | Up to 15cm →

| 1 | 2 | 3 | 4 | 5 | 6 | 7 | 8 | 9 | 10 | 11 | 12 |

• *Campanula pelviformis* Lam.

Campanula pelviformis

Endemic to the east of Crete, this plant
has erect stems which are often woody,
and hairy leaves, lanceolate, toothed
and stalked at the base. The flowers
are bluish-violet, up to 4cm, and take
the form of a 'stamna' or water jar, divided at the top into lobes which
fold backwards. The calyx has
swellings and sharply-pointed
lobes. Found on rocky slopes and
in scrub.

Eastern Crete | 10-50cm →

| 1 | 2 | 3 | 4 | 5 | 6 | 7 | 8 | 9 | 10 | 11 | 12 |

Campanula persicifolia L.
Peach-leaved bellflower

A perennial with a smooth, slender stem and lanceolate, elongated leaves with jagged edges, up to 12cm in length. The flowers along the length of the stem occur singly, without a stalk; they have a diameter of up to 4cm. The corolla is bluish-violet, bell-shaped and very open with triangular lobes. The calyx has straight lobes extending to the middle of the corolla. Found in mountain pastures and forests.

Thrace, Macedonia, Epirus, Thessaly | 30-80cm ↑ | 🔺 🌱

| 1 | 2 | 3 | 4 | 5 | 6 | 7 | 8 | 9 | 10 | 11 | 12 |

Campanula spatulata Sibth. & Sm.
Campanula spatulata

This is one of the more frequently-occurring campanulae. The basal leaves are elliptical with a long, thin stalk. The flowers are on long stalks, funnel-shaped and divided to the middle, bluish-violet to white with dark veining. The calyx has straight lobes. Found in meadows, phrygana, clearings, and on roadsides.

Distributed | Up to 50cm ↑ | 🔺 🌱 ❀

| 1 | 2 | 3 | 4 | 5 | 6 | 7 | 8 | 9 | 10 | 11 | 12 |

Campanula tubulosa Lam.

Campanula tubulosa

This is a biennial plant, hairy and with the lower leaves stalked, ovate, and toothed; the upper leaves are stalkless. Tubular flowers, bluish-violet, more rarely white, up to 3cm. The calyx has lobes extending to the middle of the corolla, with two characteristic swellings at the base of each lobe. Endemic to western Crete, preferring rocky slopes.

◄ *C. saxatilis*, which prefers old walls and cliffs as its habitat, is a hairless plant with flowers which resemble those of *C. tubulosa*; it is also endemic to western Crete.

Western Crete | 20/40cm → ↑ | ▲ ⬇ | 1 2 3 4 5 6 7 8 9 10 11 12

Campanula versicolor Sibth. & Smith.

Campanula versicolor

A perennial plant with a strong stem and leathery, heart-shaped, jagged leaves, the lower ones on a broad stalk, the upper ones stalkless. The violet, blue or white flowers have triangular lobes and a dark throat, and grow in a dense spike. Calyx with straight, sharply-tipped lobes. On rocky slopes and among ruins.

Epirus | Up to 50cm ↑ | ▲ ⬇ | 1 2 3 4 5 6 7 8 9 10 11 12

Legousia falcata (Ten.) Janch. / syn. *Specularia falcata*   CAMPANULACEAE
Spicate Venus's Looking Glass

The wild violets belong to the same family as the campanulae, with flowers that open more widely than those of the latter. *L. falcata* has slightly toothed, stalked leaves, and a stem with a loose flower spike, violet in colour, on its upper half. The calyx has very thin lobes the same length as the corolla. Found in stony locations.

Sparsely distributed | 20-50cm ↑ |

| 1 | 2 | 3 | 4 | 5 | 6 | 7 | 8 | 9 | 10 | 11 | 12 |

Legousia pentagonia (L.) Druce / syn. *Specularia pentagonia*   CAMPANULACEAE
Legousia pentagonia

An annual plant with many stems, its lower leaves inverted ovate in shape and stalked, the upper leaves stalkless. Corolla of up to 3cm and pentagonal in shape - hence its name. The calyx is downy with sharply-pointed lobes to 1/3 of the corolla. Found in stony locations and phrygana.

L. speculum-veneris is similar, but has flowers of up to 2cm.

Distributed | 10-40cm ↑ |

| 1 | 2 | 3 | 4 | 5 | 6 | 7 | 8 | 9 | 10 | 11 | 12 |

Petromarula pinnata (L.) A.DC.

Rock lettuce

This endemic plant is of great importance, since it is the only representative of its genus. The deeply-divided, toothed leaves are concentrated at the base. The flowers have gentle shading from bluish violet to white with elongated petals turned backwards in large, cluster-like spikes. A very beautiful plant, which can be seen in flower on slopes and on old walls. Its name derives from the Greek words for *pétra* = rock and *maroúli* = lettuce.

Crete | Up to 70cm ↑ |

1 2 3 4 5 6 7 8 9 10 11 12

Capparis spinosa L.
Caper

CAPPARACEAE

A small, perennial, much-branched bush which prefers cliffs and crevices in walls. It produces many intertwining stems, and has leathery, ovate to almost round, smooth, stalked leaves. The flowers are large, on a long stalk, white or pink with 4 pink or green sepals and 4 white petals, which are larger. The stamens are red and characteristically there are many of them, longer than the petals; this gives the flower its particular appearance. The little buds of the caper are collected and preserved in salt, to be used as an accompaniment to salads.

C. ovata is almost the same plant, but it has slightly downy leaves which are more ovate in shape with a little prickle - the continuation of the leaf-vein - at their tip.

Distributed | 30-100cm → | ⛰ ☁ 🏴

| 1 | 2 | 3 | 4 | 5 | 6 | 7 | 8 | 9 | 10 | 11 | 12 |

Lonicera etrusca SANTI
Honeysuckle

An evergreen bush, its stems much-branched and russet in colour, and grey-green leaves which are large (up to 8cm) and smooth. The upper leaves are fused and periblastic. The pleasantly-scented flowers occur in heads on a common stalk. Tubular corolla, two-lipped, white or pink, up to 5cm in diameter with long white stamens. Found in thickets, forests, and on rocky slopes. *L. implexa* is similar, but the head bearing the flowers is hidden by the final pair of leaves, which form a cup.

Distributed | 1-3m ↑ |

| 1 | 2 | 3 | 4 | 5 | 6 | 7 | 8 | 9 | 10 | 11 | 12 |

Sambucus ebulus L.
Dwarf elder

A bush or tree with lanceolate, saw-edged leaves. The flowers are white, with 5 sharply-pointed petals, arranged in umbels. The fruits are black berries. This is a rank-smelling plant which spreads easily, creating large populations; it is toxic and has several uses in folk medicine. Found in roadsides, in ditches, and abandoned fields.

Distributed | 60-200cm ↑ |

| 1 | 2 | 3 | 4 | 5 | 6 | 7 | 8 | 9 | 10 | 11 | 12 |

Arenaria cretica SPRENG.
Arenaria cretica

A perennial, hairy plant with spreading stems and fleshy, ovate leaves. The flowers are on long, erect stalks, white, with five petals and sepals half of the length of the petals. A very beautiful plant, forming white clumps in the crevices of rocks in the alpine zone.

Distributed | Up to 20cm →

Dianthus

A plant dedicated to Zeus, which is why the ancient Greeks named it thus (*Dias* = 'Zeus', and *ánthos* = 'flower'). This wild 'pink' is represented in Greece by more than 50 species and subspecies, in many forms from small herbaceous plants to large bushes. The flowers have a cylindrical, five-lobed calyx, and a tubular corolla with five petals, usually white or pink, toothed at the lip and with ten stamens. The leaves are usually linear. A beautiful plant, of which many types are grown for decorative purposes.

D. sphacioticus is a small wild pink with an elongated whitish-pink corolla, endemic to the White Mountains of Crete.

Dianthus cruentus GRISEB.
Dianthus cruentus

This plant has a grey-green, quadrangular stem with a height of up to 60cm. There are up to 15 flowers in hemispherical heads with a calyx that has markedly elongated lobes.

The colour of the petals ranges from deep purple to pink, and they have toothed lips. Found in mountain pastures on mainland Greece.

D. giganteus is a generally similar plant, but it is more robust, with a height that can reach to 1 metre.

Thrace, Macedonia, Epirus, Thessaly, Sterea, Peloponnese | 20-60cm ↑

Dianthus deltoides L.

Dianthus deltoides

A perennial plant, downy and with a stem of up to 40cm and narrow, straight leaves, those of the sterile stems being shorter and broader. It has rose-coloured flowers with a circle of purple and white stippling towards the centre; the petals are toothed-edged. In Greece, two more or less similar subspecies have been recognised. Found in cool pastures in the mountain zone.

Macedonia, Epirus, Thessaly | 10-40cm ↑ | 🔺 ⬇ 🌱 | 1 2 3 4 5 6 7 8 9 10 11 12

Dianthus juniperinus Sm.

Dianthus juniperinus

A phrygano plant or small bush with many branches, woody, with narrow, pointed leaves, concentrated at the base of the flower-bearing stalks. The flowers have pink petals, toothed at the edges. Seven subspecies have been described, all endemic to Crete. Found on rocky slopes and steep cliffs.

Crete | 30-80cm ↑ | 🔺 🌿 ◆ | 1 2 3 4 5 6 7 8 9 10 11 12

Minuartia verna (Boiss. & Spruner) Graebn.
Minuartia verna

These are small, grassy herbaceous plants which thrive normally at high altitudes. *M. verna* is much branched, very slightly downy to almost smooth, with small, striaght, pointed leaves. The flowers are arranged in a loose spike with sharply-pointed petals, the same length as the sepals in the subspecies *attica* which is shown here. The minuartiae are a very beautiful species, with a considerable number of subspecies.

Sterea, Peloponnese, Epirus, Crete | 5-15cm ➔ ↑ | 🔺 ⚘

| 1 | 2 | 3 | 4 | 5 | 6 | 7 | 8 | 9 | 10 | 11 | 12 |

Paronychia macrosepala Boiss.
Paronychia macrosepala

A small, grassy plant with small, opposite, lanceolate leaves. The little flowers have bracts that are very much larger, semi-transparent, silvery-yellow and membrane-like, which give the plant an ethereal appearance. The name derives from the Greek words *pará* and *nychi*, and describes the semi-transparent appearance of the bracts.

Distributed | 5-15cm ➔ ↑ | 🔺 ⚘

| 1 | 2 | 3 | 4 | 5 | 6 | 7 | 8 | 9 | 10 | 11 | 12 |

Petrorhagia velutina (Guss.) P.W.Ball & Heywood
Kohlrauschia

These plants resemble the wild pinks. *P. velutina* has a tall stem, downy, with small, linear leaves. The calyx is ovoid with flat scales and light pink petals, two-lobed with dark veining. Found in fallow fields and stony locations. The name is also of Greek origin, coming from the words *pétra* = rock, and *rígma* = crevice, which refer to the preferred biotope of some of the species.

Distributed | 10-50cm ↑ | 🔺 ⚘

| 1 | 2 | 3 | 4 | 5 | 6 | 7 | 8 | 9 | 10 | 11 | 12 |

Silene

This is one of the most populated genera in the world and is represented by more than 80 species in Greece, of which quite a number are endemic. The plants have a calyx with 5 teeth and 10 or more veins. The petals have a narrow 'fingernail' in the middle and form a paracorolla.

Silene bellidifolia.

The photograph shows *S. bellidiflora*, with the paracorolla thus formed clearly visible. The petals of the Silenes are very often rolled in spiral fashion towards the centre.

Silene colorata Poir.

CARYOPHYLLACEAE

Silene colorata

This plant prefers sandy beaches, where it often forms a beautiful pink mat. It has trailing or erect stems and small, lanceolate leaves. The flowers are on stalks and arranged in a loose spike. The calyx is cylindrical, swollen at the tip with russet-coloured stripes. The petals are pink, divided into two deep lobes. It is often to be found far away from the sea, on sandy soil.

Distributed | 10-50cm → | 1 2 3 4 5 6 7 8 9 10 11 12

Silene compacta Fisch.

CARYOPHYLLACEAE

Silene compacta

This is one of the larger silenes with a height that can exceed 1 metre; it has a robust stem, with opposite, lanceolate, stalkless leaves. The flowers have a short stalk and occur in dense hemispherical, terminal heads with a cylindrical calyx and pink unlobed petals. A beautiful, annual plant which is often grown for ornamental purposes. Found in northern Greece in fallow fields and thickets.

Macedonia, Epirus, Thessaly, Thrace | 50-120cm ↑ | 1 2 3 4 5 6 7 8 9 10 11 12

Silene cretica L.
Silene cretica

A delicate, slightly-branched annual. The lower leaves are elongated and inverted ovate in shape, the upper leaves are narrow and pointed. The calyx is smooth, narrower at the lips with green stripes. The petals are pink and divided into two lobes. Found in olive groves, uncultivated fields, and stony locations.

Distributed | 10-50cm ↑ | ▲ ↓ | 1 | 2 | 3 | 4 | 5 | 6 | 7 | 8 | 9 | 10 | 11 | 12 |

Silene gallica L.
Small-flowered catchfly

CARYOPHYLLACEAE

An annual, downy plant, with slightly branching stems and opposite leaves; the upper ones are oblong, the lower ones inverted ovate in shape. The flowers are arranged in a loose spike with an ovoid calyx, narrow at the lip, very hairy with russet-coloured stripes. The petals are pink or more rarely white, and entire. Found in rocky locations, in fields and on roadsides.

Distributed | 20-50cm ↑ | ▲ ↓ | 1 | 2 | 3 | 4 | 5 | 6 | 7 | 8 | 9 | 10 | 11 | 12 |

Silene vulgaris (MOENCH) GARCKE
Bladder campion

CARYOPHYLLACEAE

| 1 | 2 | 3 | 4 | 5 | 6 | 7 | 8 | 9 | 10 | 11 | 12 |

The most common of all the silenes, this is a perennial plant, smooth and much-branched, with stalked leaves which are lanceolate and up to 6cm; the upper leaves are stalkless. The calyx is light-coloured, beige or greenish, ovoid or almost spherical, with many veins and a mosaic-like blazon. The petals are white, two-lobed and fall easily, while the calyx remains. Found in uncultivated fields, on roadsides, and on slopes.

Distributed | Up to 100cm ↑ → | ▲ ↓

CISTACEAE

Cistus

The 'ladanies' are very beautiful evergreen shrubs which prefer sunny, dry locations. Very often – and particularly on hot days - whole slopes covered with cistus seem to breathe out their scent.The flowers, which resemble roses, have five white or pink petals and numerous yellow stamens. These are aromatic plants, and from certain species ladanum is extracted, a gum which is secreted by the leaf glands and has pharmaceutical properties. According to Dioscurides, it was collected either from the hair of goats, to which it had adhered, or with leather strips, as was still the practice on Crete in 1700, at the time when Tournefort was on his travels. Four species are found in Greece, two with white and two with pink flowers.

Cistus creticus L. / syn. *Cistus incanus ssp. creticus*

Cistus creticus

CISTACEAE

| 1 | 2 | 3 | 4 | 5 | 6 | 7 | 8 | 9 | 10 | 11 | 12 |

This is the cistus from which gum ladanum was at one time collected. It is a shrub which produces many branches with short, white, sticky hairs and stalked leaves, opposite and gland-bearing, undulating at the edges. It has flowers of up to 6cm with short sepals and pink petals of a particular shape which gives a rather untidy appearance. It is often found in large populations on stony slopes and in thickets.

Distributed | 50-100cm ↑ →

Cistus parviflorus Lamk.

Small-flowered cistus

A much-branched shrub or phryg-ano plant with characteristic sil-ver-green foliage, generally smaller and with a smaller distribution than C. creticus. The flowers do not exceed 3cm in diameter, and grow up to 6 together in umbels. The leaves are slightly downy, and billowy. Found in phrygana, thickets and pine forests.

Distributed | 40-70cm ↑→ | ⛰ 🦔 | 1 2 **3 4 5 6** 7 8 9 10 11 12

Cistus salvifolius L.

Sage-leaved cistus

This is a hairy shrub with leaves which in contrast to the other cistus shrubs are non-sticky but resemble those of the sage - hence its name. The flowers are white on long stalks with a diameter of up to 5cm; sometimes there are so many of them that they almost cover the plant. Found in phrygana and thickets.

◀ C. monspeliensis is similar but has smaller flowers, up to 3cm, and its leaves are oblong and stalkless.

Distributed | 30-90cm ↑→ | ⛰ ☁ | 1 2 **3 4 5 6** 7 8 9 10 11 12

• *Helianthemum hymettium* Boiss. & Heldr. CISTACEAE
Helianthemum hymettium

The helianthema are little plants which belong to the same family as the cistus shrubs and have flowers more or less resembling them but smaller, usually yellow and more rarely white or pink. *H. hymettium* is a small, hairy, much-branched and trailing phrygano plant with opposite leaves that are ovate-lanceolate in shape and very hairy. The flowers are yellow and stalked, with a diameter that does not exceed 1cm. Found in rocky, mountainous locations.

Sterea, Attica, Peloponnese, Crete | 5-30cm ↑ → | ▲▲ ⚘ | 1 2 3 **4** 5 **6** 7 8 9 10 11 12

COMPOSITAE

The Compositae or Asteraceae constitute the largest family in the plant kingdom. Their 'flowers' (flower-bearing heads) are in reality made up of many smaller flowers which, in the daisies for example, are of two types – those of the periphery (ray) and those of the disc. The base of each head is covered by leaflets (bracts) which are very often spiny.

● *Achillea cretica* L. COMPOSITAE
Cretan yarrow

More than 20 varieties of these very decorative plants are found in Greece which, because they are considered to have haemostatic (styptic) properties, bear the name of the Homeric hero Achilles who according to mythology gave the plant to his soldiers so that they could staunch their wounds.

A. cretica is an elegant plant with many stems and elongated, wing-like leaves. The flowers are white and form an umbel. Found in rocky locations and on slopes.

Crete, Karpathos, Aegean | 20-60cm ↑ | ▲▲ ⚓ ◈ | 1 2 3 **4** 5 **6** 7 8 9 10 11 12

Anthemis chia L.

Greek chamomile

This little daisy is the most common in Greece and embellishes the fields in spring with its whitish-yellow colours. It has deeply-divided leaves, smooth or slightly downy. The flower-heads are on long stalks and up to 4cm in diameter, with the peripheral flowers white, tongue-like and with three little lobes at the tip. The central florets are all of the same height, yellow, and form a disc. Found in fields, olive groves, and on roadsides.

Distributed | 20-60cm ↑ | 〽 ⌄ | 1 | 2 | 3 | 4 | 5 | 6 | 7 | 8 | 9 | 10 | 11 | 12 |

• *Anthemis rigida* (Sm.) Boiss. & Heldr.

Rayless chamomile

A small plant with spreading stems and deeply-divided leaves, which are slightly fleshy. The flower-heads are small, up to 1cm, with yellow florets. The peripheral florets are nearly always absent. Found in sandy and stony locations near the sea.

More than 20 species of *Anthemis* are found in Greece; some of them, isolated on small islands or in remote places, are endemic, as for example the little *A. filicaulis*, found on the far eastern tip of Crete.

A. filicaulis

Crete, Aegean | 5-10cm → | 〽 ⌄ | 1 | 2 | 3 | 4 | 5 | 6 | 7 | 8 | 9 | 10 | 11 | 12 |

Aster tripolium L.

Sea aster

An erect plant, smooth and very branching with slender stems and oblong-lanceolate leaves, slightly fleshy. The flower-heads have elongated peripheral florets, light blue or violet and up to 2cm in length. The disc florets are yellow. A beautiful plant, often occurring in clumps; it prefers damp coastal locations and lagoons, flowering in the autumn.

Distributed | 20-60cm ↑ | 🔺 ⚓

| 1 | 2 | 3 | 4 | 5 | 6 | 7 | 8 | 9 | 10 | 11 | 12 |

Atractylis gummifera L. / syn. *Carlina gummifera*

Pine thistle

A perennial plant with a very short stem and leaves in a flattened rosette, oblong and deeply-divided with spiny lobes. At the centre of the rosette there develops a single flower-bearing head with a diameter of up to 6cm; it has lanceolate thorny bracts, those in the interior alternate with violet shading. The florets are numerous, pink, and remain for some time after the leaves have shrivelled. The plant is toxic, and used in folk medicine. In times past, children used the white substance that was exuded by the plant as a form of mastic or chewing gum. Found in barren, stony locations.

Crete, Aegean, Peloponnese, Sterea | Up to 40cm → | 🔺 ⚓ ☠

| 1 | 2 | 3 | 4 | 5 | 6 | 7 | 8 | 9 | 10 | 11 | 12 |

Bellis perennis L.

Daisy

These small daisies are amongst the first to flower in winter. The plant is a perennial with ovate leaves, slightly toothed and stalked. The flower-bearing heads are up to 3cm in diameter with a long stalk that is bare or only lightly downy. The peripheral florets are lanceolate, and white with reddish 'brush-strokes' on the underside. The disc florets are yellow. Found in cool locations, fields and on roadsides.

B. annua is an annual ▶ and similar, but generally smaller.

Distributed | 15cm ↑ | ▲ ↓

| 1 | 2 | 3 | 4 | 5 | 6 | 7 | 8 | 9 | 10 | 11 | 12 |

Bellis sylvestris Cyr.

Southern daisy

The fact that this plant begins to flower from autumn onwards when no other daisy is yet im bloom, and has elongated lanceolate leaves, makes *B. sylverstris* easily recognisable. The flower-bearing heads grow on very long stalks, have a diameter of up to 4cm and resemble those of the other varieties of *bellis*. Found in fields, meadows, and olive groves.

B.longifolia, which has large, long and narrow leaves and smaller flowers, is endemic to Crete.

Distributed | 10-30cm ↑ | ▲ ↓

| 1 | 2 | 3 | 4 | 5 | 6 | 7 | 8 | 9 | 10 | 11 | 12 |

Calendula arvensis L.
Field marigold

This little calendula does not exceed 30cm in height. It has lanceolate leaves that are often slightly toothed, the lower leaves stalked. The flower-heads are up to 2cm and all the florets are orange-coloured. The name derives from the Latin *Calendae* (calendar) and refers to the long period of flowering of these plants. In former times, the tongue-like florets of the calendula were used to adulterate saffron.

C. officinalis has flowers of up to 7cm in diameter, and is very often cultivated as a decorative plant.

Distributed | 15-30cm ↑ |

| 1 | 2 | 3 | 4 | 5 | 6 | 7 | 8 | 9 | 10 | 11 | 12 |

Carlina corymbosa (Boiss.) Nyman
Flat-topped carline thistle

The carlinae are thorny plants which took their name from Charlemagne, since he was believed to have used some of them to cure his army of the plague. *C. corymbosa* is a perennial with very spiny leaves and flower-heads up to 3cm, helmet-like, with yellow florets and leaf-like bracts of brownish-yellow. It divides into two subspecies, *ssp. curetum* which is endemic to Crete, and *ssp. graeca* which has a distribution throughout Greece. Found in dry, infertile locations.

Distributed | Up to 60cm ↑ |

| 1 | 2 | 3 | 4 | 5 | 6 | 7 | 8 | 9 | 10 | 11 | 12 |

Centaurea

The centaureae are a well-populated genus which is represented in Greece by over 70 species, many of which are endemic. They are polymorphic, herbaceous or phrygano plants with flower-heads which consist of only tubular florets, those of the periphery being larger and sterile, and a very characteristic hypanth covered with spiny bracts. The genus took its name from the centaur Cheiron who tried, unsuccessfully, to heal his wounds with the 'great centaurion' which was possibly a species of centaurea.

● *Centaurea attica* Nyman

COMPOSITAE

Centaurea attica

| 1 | 2 | 3 | 4 | 5 | 6 | 7 | 8 | 9 | 10 | 11 | 12 |

This elegant centaurea is endemic to Attica and prefers mountainous, rocky locations. It is a much-branched phrygano plant with slender, erect stems, covered with white down and leaves of which the lower ones are deeply-divided, the upper ones oblong-lanceolate. It has pink florets and a hypanth of up to 1cm in diameter with eyelash-like bracts, dark at the tip and with a central spine of up to 7 mm in length.

Attica | Up to 50cm ↑

Centaurea calcitrapa L.

COMPOSITAE

Red star thistle

A biennial plant with many branches and deeply-divided, lanceolate leaves, the lower ones stalked and the upper ones narrower and stalkless. The flower-head has pink florets and a hypanth with fluted bracts, spiny and with the central spine very large and off-white in colour. Found on roadsides and on the perimeters of fields. Used in folk medicine as a febrifuge and tonic.

Distributed | 20-100cm ↑

| 1 | 2 | 3 | 4 | 5 | 6 | 7 | 8 | 9 | 10 | 11 | 12 |

Centaurea idaea Boiss. & Heldr.
Centaurea idaea

A biennial plant with many winged stems and downy leaves arranged in a rosette, the lower ones deeply divided and the upper ones entire. The flower-head is hairy with yellow florets, and the hypanth has bracts that are yellowish and spiny, the largest spine up to 3cm in length. Endemic to Crete, the plant is common in stony locations at mountain altitudes.

C. solstitialis (St. Barnaby's thistle) ▶ is similar but only has one central, branched stem.

Crete | 20-40cm ↑ | ▲ ⚓

| 1 | 2 | 3 | 4 | 5 | 6 | 7 | 8 | 9 | 10 | 11 | 12 |

Centaurea raphanina Sm. / syn. *Centaurea raphanina ssp. raphanina*
Centaurea raphanina

A perennial plant without a stem; it has smooth leaves, wing-lobed, in a prostrate rosette. The rhizome is tuberous and resembles a radish - hence its name. There are 2-4 flower-heads, pink and stalkless. The hypanth has eyelash-like bracts and a spine which is slightly larger. Found in stony places, on slopes, and in phrygana.

◀ *C. mixta* is similar to C. raphanina but it has a longer flower-stalk and bracts with longer terminal spines. It is also referred to as *C. raphanina ssp. mixta.*

Crete, Karpathos | Up to 15cm → | ▲ ⚓ ◆

| 1 | 2 | 3 | 4 | 5 | 6 | 7 | 8 | 9 | 10 | 11 | 12 |

Centaurea spinosa L.

Centaurea spinosa

C. spinosa is one of the most impressive of the centaureae. It has a much-branched stem and is extremely spiny. It has solitary flower-heads with whitish-pink florets that have violet shading at the tip. The hypanth has a diameter of less than 1cm and small, eyelash-like bracts. It forms large, beautiful hemispherical bushes, usually near the sea.

Distributed | 50-200cm ↑ → | 🔺 ☁ ◆

| 1 | 2 | 3 | 4 | 5 | 6 | 7 | 8 | 9 | 10 | 11 | 12 |

Centaurea triumfetti ALL. / syn. *Centaurea cana*

Centaurea triumfetti

This very beautiful centaurea is a perennial with an erect stem and lanceolate leaves, entire and covered with white down. The flower-heads have peripheral light blue, winged florets. The central florets are smaller and violet. The hypanth has eyelash-like bracts with silver-coloured spines, of equal length. Found in clearings and stony places, usually in the mountain zone.

Epirus | Up to 30cm ↑ | 🔺 ↯ ◆

| 1 | 2 | 3 | 4 | 5 | 6 | 7 | 8 | 9 | 10 | 11 | 12 |

Chrysanthemum coronarium L.

Crown daisy

This large daisy can reach to 1 metre in height, with a strong, branched stem, and deeply-divided leaves. The flower-heads are up to 6cm in diameter with a yellow disc and ray florets that are white or yellow, or white in the upper half and yellow in the lower. Common on roadsides and in fields, and often cultivated as a decorative plant. The tender stems of this large daisy are edible, and it is also used to make a dye.

Distributed | Up to 100cm ↑ | 🔺 ⚲ ⅡP ⚘ | 1 | 2 | 3 | 4 | 5 | 6 | 7 | 8 | 9 | 10 | 11 | 12 |

Chrysanthemum segetum L.

Corn marigold

This resembles *C. coronarium*, but it always has yellow ray florets and toothed leaves, the lower ones with large lobes, the upper ones lanceolate. The brilliant yellow of the chrysanthemums has given the name to this genus, which is made up of two Greek words *chrysós* meaning gold, and *ánthos* meaning flower.

Distributed | 20-60cm ↑ | 🔺 ⚲ | 1 | 2 | 3 | 4 | 5 | 6 | 7 | 8 | 9 | 10 | 11 | 12 |

Cichorium intybus L.
Chicory

This is a very common plant with leaves arranged in rosettes, polymorphic and often deeply divided. The stem is tall, branched and slightly downy with heads growing from the axils formed by the branches. The florets are blue and toothed at the tips. An edible plant, much favoured by the Greeks who collect the young leaves that grow from the rosettes. The name is a very old one, since Theophrastus also called the plant *cichórion*.

Distributed | 30-120cm ↑ | 🏔 ⚓ 🏴

1 2 3 4 5 6 7 8 9 10 11 12

Cichorium spinosum L.
Spiny chicory

A spiny, much-branched phrygano plant with oblong leaves, toothed or with lobes. The leaves are eaten either fresh in a salad or boiled, and for this reason are keenly gathered. The heads resemble those of C. intybus, with a diameter of up to 3cm. The woody stems of the plant were used in bygone days to cover water jars in order to prevent insects from falling into them – hence the popular name of the plant in Greek, *stamnangáthi* (*stámna* = water jar, *angáthi*= spine). Found in stony locations, from the sea right up to the mountain zone.

Distributed | 20/40cm ↑→ | 🏔 🏴

1 2 3 4 5 6 7 8 9 10 11 12

Crepis rubra L.

Pink hawksbeard

More than 20 species of crepis are found in Greece, most of them with yellow flowers except for *C. rubra* which differs in that it alone has pink flowers. Its leaves are deeply divided or toothed, the upper ones are lanceolate. The heads with pink florets are up to 4cm in diameter. These 'wild dandelions' are edible and generally prefer stony locations.

Distributed | 10-40cm ↑ | | 1 | 2 | 3 | 4 | 5 | 6 | 7 | 8 | 9 | 10 | 11 | 12 |

Crupina crupinastrum (Moris) Vis.

Crupina

An annual with a thin stem, sparsely branching, with solitary heads at the tips of the stems. The leaves are concentrated in the lower part of the plant, and are wing-like with toothed lobes. Pink florets, ovoid in the hypanth amd with blackish-red bracts. Found in fields, phrygana, and stony locations.

Distributed | 20-60cm ↑ | | 1 | 2 | 3 | 4 | 5 | 6 | 7 | 8 | 9 | 10 | 11 | 12 |

Dittrichia graveolens (L.) Greuter / syn. *Inula graveolens* COMPOSITAE
Stink aster

This is an annual plant, much-branched, and hairy, with stalkless narrow, sticky leaves. There are many flower-heads with a diameter of up to 1cm. The florets are yellow, surrounded by the bracts. The plant exudes a heavy odour of camphor, and was used in the past to repel insects. Found on roadsides, in ditches and abandoned fields.

Distributed | 20-50cm ↑

| 1 | 2 | 3 | 4 | 5 | 6 | 7 | 8 | 9 | 10 | 11 | 12 |

Dittrichia viscosa (L.) Greuter/ syn. *Inula viscosa* COMPOSITAE
Aromatic inula

This is the predominant wild flower in autumn. Often found on roadsides and in ditches, it is a decorative plant with its yellow, pyramid-shaped flower spikes. It has elongated leaves, which are lanceolate and sticky. The spike has many heads on long flower stalks. The florets are yellow, the ray florets tongue-like and toothed at the tip. A plant used as a dye, producing beautiful shades of green.

Distributed | 0,40-1m ↑

| 1 | 2 | 3 | 4 | 5 | 6 | 7 | 8 | 9 | 10 | 11 | 12 |

Doronicum columnae Tem.

COMPOSITAE

Doronicum columnae

A perennial with long, erect stems. The lower leaves are large, kidney-shaped and toothed on a long stalk, the upper leaves are stalkless and periblastic. The flower heads are solitary, at the tips of the stems with a diameter of up to 5cm. The florets are yellow, the ray florets ribbon-like. Found in shady, woodland locations in the mountain zone.

Thrace, Macedonia, Epirus, Thessaly | 30-60cm ↑ | 🔺 ⚓

| 1 | 2 | 3 | 4 | 5 | 6 | 7 | 8 | 9 | 10 | 11 | 12 |

Echinops spinosissimus Turra

COMPOSITAE

Spiny globe thistle

A perennial, with a smooth, white, branching stem. The leaves are deeply divided with spiny lobes. It has spherical flower-heads with white or bluish-violet florets surrounded by light green spiny bracts. Found in dry, stony locations. The name *Echinops* derives from the Greek and refers to the spiny appearance of the flower-heads.

Distributed | 0,50-1m ↑ | 🔺 ⚓

| 1 | 2 | 3 | 4 | 5 | 6 | 7 | 8 | 9 | 10 | 11 | 12 |

Erigeron glabratus Hoppe & Hornsch.

Erigeron glabratus

A small, beautiful plant with smooth leaves, oblong-lanceolate, and eyelash-like. The stems are up to 10cm long with 1-2 flower-bearing heads, similar to those of the aster, which have a yellow disc and ribbon-like, light pink ray florets. E. alpinus is similar to E. glabratus and likewise found in stony places and at alpine altitudes. The name *Erigeron* comes from the Greek words which mean 'old man's hair', and refers to the pappus of the plant, i.e. to the appearance of the head after the ripening of the seeds, which have hairs so that they can be dispersed by the wind.

Sterea, Thessaly, Macedonia, Crete | Up to 10cm ↑ |

| 1 | 2 | 3 | 4 | 5 | 6 | 7 | 8 | 9 | 10 | 11 | 12 |

Galactites tomentosa Moench.

Galactites

A common plant, taking its name from the white veins in the leaves which look as if they are filled with milk. It has an erect, downy stem and stalkless, deeply-divided leaves which are hairy on the underside and have spines at the tips of the lobes. The flower-head is ovoid with spiny bracts, covered with spidery hairs. The florets are pink or white. Found on roadsides, and in abandoned fields.

Distributed | 30-80cm ↑ |

| 1 | 2 | 3 | 4 | 5 | 6 | 7 | 8 | 9 | 10 | 11 | 12 |

Helichrysum doerfleri Rᴇᴄʜ.

Helichrysum

This little Helichrysum is a rare plant threatened with extinction, since its biotope extends over only a few square metres on Mount Thrypti in eastern Crete. It has short stems and oblong-lanceolate leaves, of which the upper ones are ovate, all covered with a dense white down. The flower-heads are very beautiful, with silvery-red bracts of a pearly texture. The florets are of a brilliant yellow colour, as is the case with all the Helichrysa, and it is this which gives the genus its name, deriving from the Greek words *helios* (sun) and *chrysós* (gold).

Crete | Up to 10cm →

| 1 | 2 | 3 | 4 | 5 | 6 | 7 | 8 | 9 | 10 | 11 | 12 |

Helichrysum italicum (Rᴏᴛʜ) G. Dᴏɴ ꜰɪʟ. / syn. *H. microphyllum*

Helichrysum italicum

This is one of the more widely distributed amaranths. It is a much-branched, aromatic plant, and has small, linear leaves covered with dense white down. The ovoid flower-bearing heads form dense clumps at the tips of the stems and have yellow florets, covered with greyish-yellow bracts. Found in stony places from the edge of the sea up to the mountain zone.

Aegean, Crete | 20-50cm ↑ |

| 1 | 2 | 3 | 4 | 5 | 6 | 7 | 8 | 9 | 10 | 11 | 12 |

Helichrysum stoechas (L.) Moench / syn. *H. barrelieri* COMPOSITAE
Helichrysum stoechas

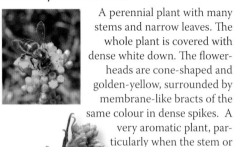

A perennial plant with many stems and narrow leaves. The whole plant is covered with dense white down. The flower-heads are cone-shaped and golden-yellow, surrounded by membrane-like bracts of the same colour in dense spikes. A very aromatic plant, particularly when the stem or leaves are cut. Found in phrygana and stony locations.

◀ *H. heldreichii* is a more or less similar plant to H. stoechas and endemic to the Samaria Gorge of Crete.

Distributed | 10-50cm ↑ |

| 1 | 2 | 3 | 4 | 5 | 6 | 7 | 8 | 9 | 10 | 11 | 12 |

Inula crithmoides L. COMPOSITAE
Golden samphire

This flowers in the autumn and prefers seashores and damp, brackish areas. It is a smooth plant with many erect stems and leaves in clusters, narrow and fleshy. The flower-heads measure from 2 to 3cm in size; the ray florets are yellow, the disc florets orange.

Distributed | 30-40cm ↑ |

| 1 | 2 | 3 | 4 | 5 | 6 | 7 | 8 | 9 | 10 | 11 | 12 |

Notobasis syriaca (L.) Cᴀss.
Syrian thistle

A thistle with a robust stem similar to the 'gaidourángathi' (donkey thistle). The leaves are deeply divided, with white veins and spiny lobes, smooth on the upper surface, downy on the underside. Spherical heads with alternate bracts, needle-pointed, surrounded by large spines. The florets are all tubular and pink. Found in infertile, uncultivated locations.

Distributed | 20-120cm ↑ |

| 1 | 2 | 3 | 4 | 5 | 6 | 7 | 8 | 9 | 10 | 11 | 12 |

Onopordum illyricum L.
Illyrian Scotch thistle

The etymology of the names given to plants often shows an inclination towards humour; in the case of *Onopordum* (donkey thistle), for example, this is the scientific name assigned to it by *Linnaeus*. It comes from two Greek words , *ónos* = donkey and *pérdomai* = fart, which refer to the effect that it was supposed to have on the animal. The Onoporda are plants with a strong stem, and very spiny. They have large, spherical flower-heads with many pink florets. *O. illyricum* has winged-lobed leaves which are spiny, and flower-heads up to 6cm with bracts shorter than the florets. Found in barren locations.

Distributed | 50-130cm ↑ |

| 1 | 2 | 3 | 4 | 5 | 6 | 7 | 8 | 9 | 10 | 11 | 12 |

Onopordum tauricum Willd.

Onoporium tauricum

COMPOSITAE

This plant can reach a height of 2 metres. It has a spiny, winged stem. The leaves are large, deeply divided, hairy at first and then smooth. The heads are up to 7cm in size, spherical and with flat bracts at the base, longer than the pink florets. Found in abandoned fields, ditches and on roadsides.

Distributed | 100-200cm ↑ | 🏔 ⚓

| 1 | 2 | 3 | 4 | 5 | 6 | 7 | 8 | 9 | 10 | 11 | 12 |

Otanthus maritimus (L.) Hoffmanns. & Link

Cottonweed

COMPOSITAE

A perennial shrub with a preference for sandy coastlines, thus also for beaches. There are many erect stems, and lanceolate leaves, stalkless and entire. The whole plant is covered by dense, cotton-like down. The heads are round with tubular, yellow florets. The two swellings (little ears) at the base of the corolla give this plant its name, from the Greek words *otíon* (little ear) and *ánthos* (flower).

Distributed | Up to 50cm ↑ | 🏔 ☁

| 1 | 2 | 3 | 4 | 5 | 6 | 7 | 8 | 9 | 10 | 11 | 12 |

Pallenis spinosa (L.) Cass. / syn. *Asteriscus spinosus*   COMPOSITAE
Pallenis spinosa

A biennial with a branching stem, very downy. The leaves are elongated and lanceolate, downy, and concave, the upper ones stalkless. The flower-heads have spiny bracts, similar to the leaves, the inside bracts being shorter. The disc is yellow and up to 2cm, with ray florets that are tongue-shaped, yellow or russet-coloured. Found in fields, rocky locations, and olive groves.

Distributed | Up to 60cm ↑ | ▲ ⬇ | 1 | 2 | 3 | 4 | 5 | 6 | 7 | 8 | 9 | 10 | 11 | 12 |

Phagnalon graecum Bois. & Heldr.   COMPOSITAE
Phagnalon

A perennial phrygano plant with many stems and oblong-lanceolate leaves with undulating edges, all very downy. The flower-heads are at the tips of the stems, solitary, and are rounded with narrow, needle-like bracts which are pointed at the tips, and yellow florets. It is usually found on rocky slopes.

P. pygmaeum is similar but a much smaller plant with smooth, spade-like leaves. It is endemic to the mountains of Crete.

Distributed | 10-40cm ↑ | ▲ ▬ | 1 | 2 | 3 | 4 | 5 | 6 | 7 | 8 | 9 | 10 | 11 | 12 |

Ptilostemon chamaepeuce (L.) Less.

COMPOSITAE

Shrubby ptilostemon

This small, downy shrub has very characteristic needle-like leaves, similar to those of the pine. The heads are ovoid with scale-like downy bracts, sharply pointed. The florets are tubular, pink and more rarely white. Found on steep rocky cliffs and slopes. The name of this elegant plant epitomizes the use of Greek words in the nomenclature of plants. The name of the genus originates from the words *ptílon* (downy wing) and *stímon* (stamen) and refers to the downy stamens of the plant, while the species is described with the word *chamaí* (low) and *péfki* (pine) which describe the general appearance of the plant as that of a low pine-tree.

Distributed | 30-100cm ↑ |

| 1 | 2 | 3 | 4 | 5 | 6 | 7 | 8 | 9 | 10 | 11 | 12 |

Scolymus hispanicus L.

COMPOSITAE

Spanish oyster plant

An annual herbaceous plant with branching, winged stems, very spiny. The leaves are wing-lobed, spiny and with white veining. The flower-heads grow from the axils of the stems and have spiny bracts and tongue-like yellow florets. Both the tender stems of the plant and the roots are edible. Found in barren places, from the sea up to the semi-mountainous zone.

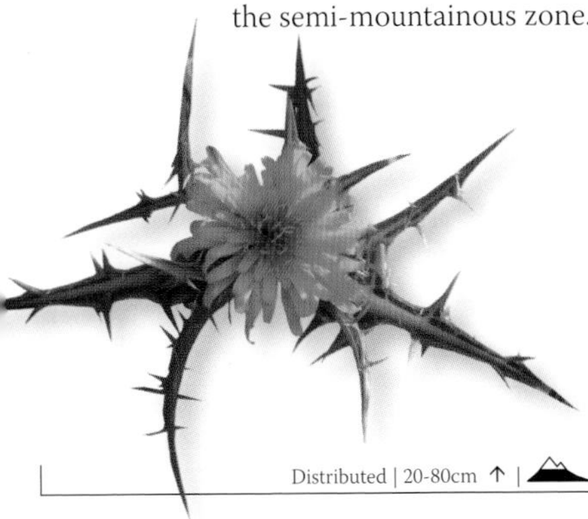

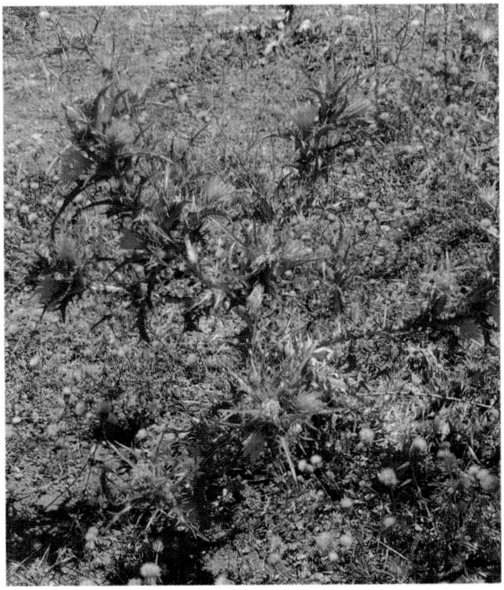

Distributed | 20-80cm ↑ |

1	2	3	4	5	6	7	8	9	10	11	12

• *Scorzonera cretica* L.

COMPOSITAE

Cretan viper's grass

A variform, perennial herbaceous plant with many stems, erect and downy. The narrow, linear leaves are up to 1cm in width, most of them concentrated at the base of the plant. The heads are brownish-red with all the florets yellow and tongue-like. Found on slopes, roadsides, and in rocky places.

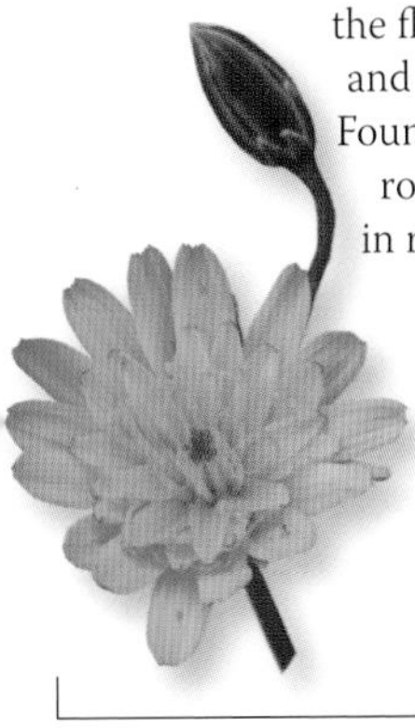

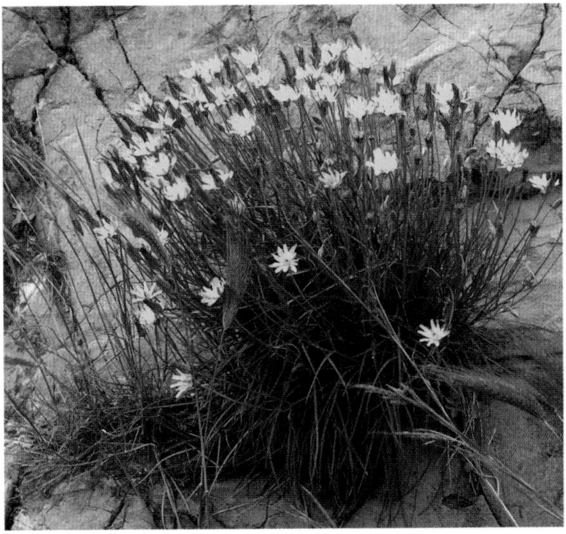

Aegean, Crete, Rhodes | Up to 30cm → |

1	2	3	4	5	6	7	8	9	10	11	12

Scorzonera crocifolia Sibth. & Sm.

Scorzonera crocifolia

This plant is more or less similar to S. cretica, but with narrower leaves which are fluted and have a light-coloured line at the centre, resembling those of the crocus. The heads are greenish with tongue-like, yellow florets. Found in stony places and on roadsides.

Thessaly, Attica, Sterea, Peloponnese | Up to 30cm ↑ | 🔺 ⚓

| 1 | 2 | 3 | 4 | 5 | 6 | 7 | 8 | 9 | 10 | 11 | 12 |

Silybum marianum (L.) Gaertn.

Holy thistle, milk thistle

A biennial plant, with strongly-branched, wand-like stems. The leaves are large with undulating, spiny edges and develop in rosettes during the first year. According to tradition, the white spots and veins of the plant were caused by the milk of the Virgin Mary – hence the name *marianum*. The heads have large, spiny bracts and all of the florets are tubular and pink in colour. Found on the margins of fields, in ditches, and on roadsides.

Distributed | 0,20-1,50m ↑ | 🔺 ⚓ 🌢 💮

| 1 | 2 | 3 | 4 | 5 | 6 | 7 | 8 | 9 | 10 | 11 | 12 |

Staehelina arborea SCHREB. / syn. *Staehelina petiolata* COMPOSITAE

Staehelina arborea

A small bush with a woody stem which gives it a tree-like form. The leaves are typically long, downy-stalked, large, ovate, smooth and green on the upper surface, with white down on the underside. The heads are oblong, cylindrical and scaly with all florets cylindrical, and pink in colour. This plant is usually found in ravines, where it prefers sheer slopes and crevices in the rocks.

Crete | 20-80cm ↑ | ▲ ◼ ◆ | 1 | 2 | 3 | 4 | 5 | 6 | 7 | 8 | 9 | 10 | 11 | 12 |

Staehelina fruticosa L. COMPOSITAE

Staehelina fruticosa

A small bush or phrygano plant with lanceolate leaves which are smooth, fleshy and many in number, the lower ones having a little stalk. The flower-bearing heads resemble those of *S. arborea*, but the florets are white and it flowers later. Found in similar biotopes.

Aegean, Crete | 20-100cm ↑ | ▲ ◆ ◼ ◆ | 1 | 2 | 3 | 4 | 5 | 6 | 7 | 8 | 9 | 10 | 11 | 12 |

Tragopogon hybridus L. / syn. *Geropogon hybridus* COMPOSITAE
Tragopogon hybridus

A plant with a thin, smooth stem, and periblastic leaves which are straight-lanceolate, pointed at the tip. The heads have 5-8 bracts, at least double the number of the light pink florets which themselves occur in an even number. The whole appearance of the flower resembles that of a star. Found in fields, meadows, and on roadsides. The name of this genus originates from the Greek words *trágos* (goat) and *pigoúni* (beard); it refers to the shape of the pappus and was already used by Theophrastus and Dioscurides.

Distributed | 20-50cm ↑ |

1	2	3	4	5	6	7	8	9	10	11	12

Tragopogon porrifolius L. / syn. *Tragopogon sinuatus* COMPOSITAE
Salsify, Goat's Beard

A more robust plant than the latter with broad, linear, periblastic leaves. The flower-heads contain many florets, pink or violet with sharply-pointed bracts which are either the same length or longer than the ray florets. After flowering, the bracts close and re-open to release the winged seeds. The roots of the plant are edible. It is common in the lowland zone.

Distributed | 20-80cm ↑ |

1	2	3	4	5	6	7	8	9	10	11	12

Calystegia sepium (L.) R. Br.
Hedge bindweed

CONVOLVULACEAE

A perennial climber with large dart- to heart-shaped and slightly undulating leaves. The flowers are white, solitary and up to 5cm with a short stalk, growing in the leaf axils. A very decorative plant which is often cultivated on fences. Found in moist, shady areas, by streams, and in thickets. The two bracts which enclose the calyx like a roof give the name to this plant (calyx + *stégi*, i.e. roof).

C. soldanella is a trailing plant with rose-like flowers and kidney-shaped leaves. It prefers sandy beaches.

Distributed | Up to 3m ↑→ | 🔺 🌿 🌱

| 1 | 2 | 3 | 4 | 5 | 6 | 7 | 8 | 9 | 10 | 11 | 12 |

Convolvulus althaeoides L.
Mallow-leaved bindweed

CONVOLVULACEAE

A perennial plant, hairy, normally trailing or a climber. The leaves take a number of forms; the lower ones are heart-shaped with shallow lobes, the upper ones palm-lobed with a larger central lobe. The flowers resemble those of Calystegia – pink and darker at the centre. The two bracts are of a rather lower height than that of the calyx. Found in rocky locations and on slopes.

Distributed | Up to 1m ↑→ | 🔺 🌿

| 1 | 2 | 3 | 4 | 5 | 6 | 7 | 8 | 9 | 10 | 11 | 12 |

Convolvulus elegantissimus Mill.

CONVOLVULACEAE

Convolvulus elegantissimus

This plant resembles C. althaeoides and is considered a subspecies of the latter by some authorities. It differs in the colour of the leaves which are silvery-green, and in the flowers which are light-coloured at the centre. Found on roadsides, slopes and cliffs.

Distributed | Up to 1m ↑ → |

1 2 3 4 5 6 7 8 9 10 11 12

● *Convolvulus oleifolius* Desr.

CONVOLVULACEAE

Convolvulus oleifolius

A perennial with a woody stem and leaves which are lanceolate-straight, silver in colour and resembling those of the olive. The flowers are light pink and up to 3cm in diameter, in terminal spikes. Found in stony locations and phrygana, often near the sea.

◀ *C. argyrothamnos* is similar to C. oleifolius but has white flowers. It is endemic to Crete and only very few occurrences have been recorded.

Sterea, Peloponnese, Crete | 10-50cm ↑ → |

1 2 3 4 5 6 7 8 9 10 11 12

Rosularia serrata (L.) A. BERGER

CRASSULACEAE

Rosularia serrata

A fleshy plant resembling *Umbilicus*. It has an erect stem with ovate, fleshy leaves that are stalkless and arranged in a basal rosette. The flowers have stalks; they are five-part, bell-like, and white with red stippling. The lobes and calyx are sharply-pointed. There are loose flower–spikes along the whole length of the stem. Normally found in shady places, on rocky slopes.

Crete, Rhodes, Aegean | Up to 30cm ↑ |

| 1 | 2 | 3 | 4 | 5 | 6 | 7 | 8 | 9 | 10 | 11 | 12 |

Sedum album L.

CRASSULACEAE

White stonecrop

The Sedum family comprises herbaceous plants with fleshy leaves known by the common folk name of 'amaranths'. *S. album* has an erect stem with alternate, ovate leaves, flat on the upper surface. The flowers have five white or slightly pinkish petals with pink veining, and develop in terminal clusters. The plant often grows in dense clumps. Found in rocky locations in the mountain and alpine zone.

Distributed | Up to 25cm ↑ |

| 1 | 2 | 3 | 4 | 5 | 6 | 7 | 8 | 9 | 10 | 11 | 12 |

Sedum littoreum Guss.

CRASSULACEAE

Sedum littoreum

A small fleshy plant with a stem that is thinner at the base and spoon-shaped leaves with russet stippling. The flowers are yellow with linear, lanceolate petals, sharply pointed at the tip, and sepals which are a little shorter. Found normally on rocks and, despite its name, it is met right up to the mountain zone.

◀

S. laconicum has more or less the same flowers, but it differs in the colour of its leaves, which are green.

Sterea, Attica, Crete | Up to 10cm ↑ |

| 1 | 2 | 3 | 4 | 5 | 6 | 7 | 8 | 9 | 10 | 11 | 12 |

Sedum rubens L.

CRASSULACEAE

Sedum rubens

A plant with a low habit, glandular and hairy with russet-coloured fleshy leaves, the lower ones opposite, often in rosettes, and the upper ones alternate. The flowers resemble those of *S. album* but the petals are sharply pointed at the tip. Found at all altitudes, normally in rock crevices.

Distributed | 4-15cm ↑ |

| 1 | 2 | 3 | 4 | 5 | 6 | 7 | 8 | 9 | 10 | 11 | 12 |

Umbilicus horizontalis (Guss.) DC.

Pennywort

A perennial, russet-coloured fleshy plant with a flower-spike in a long cluster and small tubular flowers, horizontally carried and with a short calyx. The leaves at the base are stalked, kidney-shaped, and sparsely toothed, the upper ones small and straight like bracts. Found in rocky locations, in walls and amidst ruins.

U. rupestris is similar but has drooping flowers and a calyx extending up to the middle of the corolla.

Distributed | 10-60cm↑ |

| 1 | 2 | 3 | 4 | 5 | 6 | 7 | 8 | 9 | 10 | 11 | 12 |

Umbilicus parviflorus (Desf.) DC.

Small-flowered navelwort

A perennial, fleshy plant with an erect stem, russet-coloured and with fleshy, kidney-shaped leaves, the lower ones stalked, the upper ones almost periblastic. The flowers are small and grow in short axillary clusters. The petals are yellow and double the length of the sepals. Found in rocky locations, and in dry stone walls. The name derives from the Latin word *umbilicus* ('navel'), and refers to the shape of the leaves.

Distributed | 10-40cm↑ |

| 1 | 2 | 3 | 4 | 5 | 6 | 7 | 8 | 9 | 10 | 11 | 12 |

Aethionema saxatile (L.) R. Br
CRUCIFERAE
Burnt candytuft

A perennial plant, much-branched and with a woody base. The leaves are ovate or lanceolate and fleshy, growing along the whole length of the stem, with the flowers in dense clusters at the tip. There are 4 petals, pink or white. Normally found on rocky slopes in the mountain zone. The unusual name of the plant derives from the leaves which at maturity appear burnt; it comes from the Greek *aithó* (to burn) and *níma* (thread), the latter referring to its thin stems.

A. saxatile ssp. saxatile

A. saxatile ssp. creticum

Macedonia, Thessaly, Attica, Sterea, Crete | 8-25cm↑→ | 1 2 3 4 5 6 7 8 9 10 11 12

Alyssum saxatile L. / syn. *Aurinia saxatilis*
CRUCIFERAE
Golden alyssum

The most frequently occurring of its family, *A. saxatile* is a perennial plant, polymorphic, with stalked lower leaves which are lanceolate with shallow lobes, and upper leaves that are lanceolate and stalkless. The flowers are arranged in terminal clusters and have 4 brilliant yellow petals, which are two-lobed. As its name suggests, the plant prefers rocky locations and is found frequently on slopes in the mountain zone.

Alyssum is generally a dwarf plant. More ▶ than 30 species are found in Greece, many of them endemic. *A. sphacioticum* is one of the latter, flowering in the summer at alpine altitudes in the White Mountains of Crete.

Distributed | 10-30cm ↑ | | 1 2 3 4 5 6 7 8 9 10 11 12

Arabis alpina L.
Arabis alpina

This little herbaceous plant is a perennial which prefers alpine altitudes. It is densely haired with ovate-spatulate leaves that are lightly toothed and arranged in small rosettes. The stems are erect with flowers in loose clusters. The flowers have 4 petals, up to 1cm, and are white; their length is double that of the sepals. The plant is normally found in rock crevices.

◀ *A.verna* is a plant which prefers lower altitudes and has violet-coloured flowers. The stems are long with heart-shaped, toothed and periblastic leaves.

Distributed | 10-35cm ↑ |

| 1 | 2 | 3 | 4 | 5 | 6 | 7 | 8 | 9 | 10 | 11 | 12 |

Aubrieta deltoidea D.C.
Aubrieta

This is one of the most beautiful wild flowers of the mountain zone. It is a grassy plant and often forms little cushions. The leaves are spatulate-rhomboidal, downy and loosely toothed. The flowers are violet or pink with a yellow throat. Two of the 4 sepals bear a little swelling. It is to be found in rock crevices, and is often cultivated as a decorative plant.

It was named after the artist *Claude Aubriet*, a companion of Tournefort on his journey to the East.

Macedonia, Epirus, Thessaly, Sterea, Peloponnese, Aegean, Crete | 10-20cm ↑→ |

| 1 | 2 | 3 | 4 | 5 | 6 | 7 | 8 | 9 | 10 | 11 | 12 |

Biscutella didyma L.
Biscutella didyma

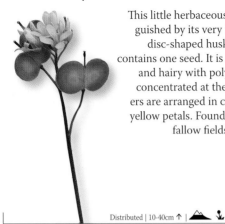

This little herbaceous plant is distinguished by its very typical twinned, disc-shaped husks of which each contains one seed. It is an annual, erect and hairy with polymorphic leaves concentrated at the base. The flowers are arranged in clusters and have yellow petals. Found in rocky places, fallow fields, and phrygana.

Distributed | 10-40cm ↑ | ▲ ↓

| 1 | 2 | 3 | 4 | 5 | 6 | 7 | 8 | 9 | 10 | 11 | 12 |

Brassica cretica LAM.
Brassica cretica

A herbaceous plant with large, fleshy grey-green leaves. The flowers have 4 white or whitish-yellow petals in a large, dense and erect cluster. This is an impressive plant which prefers sheer, rocky slopes. It is edible and particularly during difficult times in the past has constituted a basic dietary component along with other wild greens.

◀ B. nigra is similar, with yellow flowers, and is also edible; it is frequently cultivated. Its seeds were once used in the preparation of mustard.

Crete, Aegean, Peloponnese | Up to 60cm ↑ | ▲ ↓ Ⱳ

| 1 | 2 | 3 | 4 | 5 | 6 | 7 | 8 | 9 | 10 | 11 | 12 |

Cakile maritima Scop.
Sea rocket

CRUCIFERAE

This is an annual, smooth plant, with branching stems which are either trailing or climbing, and fleshy leaves, deeply divided and with lobes of uneven length that often have yellowish-red shading. The flower has 4 petals that are white or have slight violet shading and an equal number of unlobed sepals, two of them with a hump. In folk medicine the plant is used as a diuretic. It is common on sandy beaches.

Distributed | 20-50cm ↑→ | 🛆 ⚓ ∎   1 2 3 4 5 6 7 8 9 10 11 12

Cardaria draba (L.) Desv. / syn. *Lepidium draba*
Hoary cress

CRUCIFERAE

A tall plant with strong, branching stems, common on roadsides and amongst rubble. The leaves are wide, ovate or lanceolate, and toothed; the lower ones are stalked, the upper ones periblastic. The flowers are small and numerous, white and in a fan-shaped head. The name of the genus derives from the Greek word *kardiá* ('heart') and refers to the shape of the pericarp, while *draba* originates from Dioscurides and refers rather to the appearance of the plant itself.

Distributed | Up to 1m ↑ | 🛆 ⚓   1 2 3 4 5 6 7 8 9 10 11 12

Erysimum candicum ssp. *candicum* Snogerup

CRUCIFERAE

Erysimum candicum

This plant with its robust stem prefers steep rocky slopes and flowers from February onwards. The leaves are narrow, lanceolate and have a strong, light-coloured vein; they are up to 15cm in length. Most of them are concentrated at the base and form a rosette. The flowers are in terminal clusters and have 4 brilliant yellow petals and green sepals.

Crete, Aegean | 20-40cm ↑ | 🠕 🠗

| 1 | 2 | 3 | 4 | 5 | 6 | 7 | 8 | 9 | 10 | 11 | 12 |

Malcolmia flexuosa Sibth. & Sm.

CRUCIFERAE

Malcolmia flexuosa

An annual, slightly downy with fleshy, ovate-elliptical leaves. The flowers have a diameter of up to 2.5cm, with 4 pink or violet petals which have dark veining and a yellow throat. The seeds are in flexible pods with a length of up to 8cm. Normally found on sands and rocks near the sea.

Distributed | 10-35cm ↑ | 🠕 🠗

| 1 | 2 | 3 | 4 | 5 | 6 | 7 | 8 | 9 | 10 | 11 | 12 |

Matthiola sinuata (L.) R.Br.

CRUCIFERAE

Sea stock

A biennial plant, erect and with many leaves at the base which are deeply divided, with round lobes and a lip that is turned upwards, whence it derives its name. The upper leaves are linear and undulating. The flowers are violet and pleasantly-scented, up to 2.5cm in diameter. A beautiful plant, which prefers rocky slopes near the sea. It is cultivated for decoration.

Distributed | 20-80cm ↑ | ⛰ ⚓ ◆ 🌱 | 1 | 2 | 3 | 4 | 5 | 6 | 7 | 8 | 9 | 10 | 11 | 12 |

Matthiola tricuspidata (L.) R.Br.

CRUCIFERAE

Three-horned stock

An annual with herbaceous-type stems, erect or trailing. The leaves are downy, deeply divided with round lobes. The flower has a diameter of up to 1.5cm and is pink or violet, lighter-coloured at the centre. The husk which encloses the fruit has three horns at the apex, a characteristic which gives its name to the plant. Found near the sea, on sand or on rocky promontories.

Distributed | 7-40cm ↑ | ⛰ ⚓ | 1 | 2 | 3 | 4 | 5 | 6 | 7 | 8 | 9 | 10 | 11 | 12 |

CUCURBITACEAE

Bryonia cretica L.

CUCURBITACEAE

White bryony

A unisexual plant, hairy and climbing with the help of spiral tendrils similar to those of the vine. It has palmately-lobed leaves with white veining, lighter-coloured on the underside. The flowers are yellow-green with dark veining and the seed pod is red. In the female plants the inflorescences do not contain more than 1 or 2 flowers. This is a poisonous plant which prefers hedges and thickets.

B. dioica is very similar, but easily differentiated by the absence of white veining on the leaves.

Crete, Aegean, Peloponnese, Attica | Up to 4m ↑ |

Ecballium elaterium Rich.

CUCURBITACEAE

Squirting cucumber

A trailing perennial herbaceous plant, fleshy and very bristly with triangular leaves, toothed and hairy on the underside. The flowers are yellow and bloom in the leaf axils, the male flowers in clusters, the female flowers singly. The fruit is cylindrical and ovoid, up to 5cm in length, and very bristly. Of particular interest is the way in which

the plant disperses its seeds. The fruit is very sensitive and at the slightest touch it bursts like a little bomb and throws its seeds far away; it 'uncoils' like a watch-spring. This is a poisonous plant with uses in folk medicine. It is common in fallow fields, amidst rubble, and on roadsides.

Distributed | Up to 1m → |

Scabiosa hymettia BOISS. & SPRUN. / syn. *Lomelosia hymettia*   DIPSACACEAE
Scabiosa hymettia

This is a beautiful perennial shrub with slender stems, erect and downy. The leaves have lanceolate lobes, the lower leaves are lanceolate and entire. The flower-bearing heads are solitary with a diameter up to 4cm, at the tips of the stems. The florets are pinkish-violet, the ray florets being somewhat larger than those at the centre. Found in stony places.

Aegean, Sterea, Attica, Peloponnese | Up to 40/80cm ↑→ | 🔺 ⬛ | 1 2 3 **4 5 6 7** 8 9 10 11 12

Scabiosa maritima L. / syn. *Scabiosa atropurpurea, Sixalix atropurpurea*   DIPSACACEAE
Mournful widow

Despite the name, this plant is found at greater altitudes. It has long, slender stems and dissected leaves; the upper leaves are entire. The flower-heads are up to 5cm in diameter; the florets have five lobes and are violet, pink or white in colour, the ray florets being much larger. Found in dry, wasteland locations.

◀ *Knautia integrifolia.* Plants of this genus resemble the scabiouses, but they are easily differentiated by their florets, which have four lobes.

Distributed | 20-60cm ↑ | 🔺 ↓ | 1 2 3 **4 5** 6 **7** 8 9 10 11 12

Arbutus andrachne L.

ERICACEAE

Eastern strawberry tree

This plant has dark green leaves which are lanceolate, slightly toothed, and membranous. The flowers are small and off-white, in short inflorescences. The fruits are smaller than those of *A. unedo* and are not edible. Of particular interest is the trunk which sheds its thin skin in long strips to reveal an impressive red and silky-textured surface.

A natural hybrid between *A. andrachne* and *A. unedo* has been designated *A.* x *adrachnoides*.

Distributed | More than 5m ↑

| 1 | 2 | 3 | 4 | 5 | 6 | 7 | 8 | 9 | 10 | 11 | 12 |

Arbutus unedo L.

Strawberry tree

A beautiful bush or tree with light green leaves, lanceolate and slightly toothed. The flowers are white or pink, bell-shaped and arranged in dense nodding spikes which appear in autumn or sometimes in spring; thus the simultaneous occurrence of fruits and flowers is not rare. The fruits – the arbutus berries – are red, spherical with a diameter of up to 2cms and very tasty, although indigestible according to Dioscurides. The epithet 'unedo' is nothing other than a combination of two Latin words – *unus* (one) and *edo* (eat), which exactly suggest that consumption of them should be moderate! The tree is found in thickets in Mediterranean maquis, often in large populations.

Distributed | 1,5-10m ↑ | 1 2 3 4 5 6 7 8 9 10 11 12

Erica manipuliflora SALISB.

Erica manipuliflora

1 2 3 4 5 6 7 8 9 10 11 12

Autumn heather is a small phrygano-like shrub, either spreading or erect in habit, much-branched with a woody base. The leaves are small and linear, grass-green in colour and arranged in whorls. The flowers are numerous and small, bell-like and pink in long spikes. Found in thickets and phrygana, often covering large areas and giving colour to a monotonous autumnal landscape.

◄ Tree heather (*E. arborea*) is a bush or tree which can reach to 3 metres in height. It blooms in the spring and has white flowers.

Distributed | Up to 80cm ↑ |

Euphorbia

The euphorbiae or spurges as they are commonly known are a large, polymorphic genus ranging from dwarf plants to small trees. More than 40 species are represented in Greece, many of which are widely distributed. All of the euphorbiae produce a milky juice which is an irritant and poisonous, as is the rest of the plant. Very typical are the flower spikes in which the male and female flowers are protected by two bracts which form a cup. The euphorbiae took their name from Euphorbus, a Greek physician of the 1st century AD who used their milky juice for medicinal purposes.

The dwarf *E. rechingeri* is perhaps the smallest euphorbia. It is endemic to the White Mountains and prefers alpine altitudes, where it grows amongst the rocks.

● *Euphorbia acanthothamnos* Heldr. & Sart. ex Boiss.   EUPHORBIACEAE
Greek spiny spurge

A perennial, cushion-like shrub with many spiny branches. The leaves are elliptical and up to 2cm long, with the bracts like a cup. The umbel has 3-4 rays which in the year after flowering transform into spines. It is common in stony locations and probably endemic to Greece. The name comes from the Greek meaning 'thorny bush' and gives an accurate picture of this plant.

Distributed | 10-30cm ↑ | ▲▲ ▲ ☠ | 1 | 2 | 3 | 4 | 5 | 6 | 7 | 8 | 9 | 10 | 11 | 12 |

Euphorbia characias L.

Large Mediterranean spurge

The most common of the euphorbiae, this is a plant with many erect, strong stems, which are denuded at the base. The leaves are numerous, grey, lanceolate and elongated. The umbel is dense and the cups hemispherical with dark red glands. The name originates from Dioscurides and refers to the stony or rocky biotopes preferred by the plant (*hárakas* = rock).

Distributed | 30-80cm ↑ | 🏔 ⚓ ☠

| 1 | 2 | 3 | 4 | 5 | 6 | 7 | 8 | 9 | 10 | 11 | 12 |

Euphorbia dendroides L.

Tree spurge

| 1 | 2 | 3 | 4 | 5 | 6 | 7 | 8 | 9 | 10 | 11 | 12 |

One of the more beautiful euphorbiae with thick, denuded stems which give a tree-like appearance to the plant. The leaves are lanceolate and elongated; after flowering they take on an orange shade and thereafter, during the course of the summer, are shed. The umbel has a few rays and yellowish-green bracts, triangular and interdivided. Found in rocky and infertile areas, often in large populations.

Distributed | Up to 2m ↑ | 🏔 🌳 ☠

Euphorbia helioscopia L.

EUPHORBIACEAE

Sun spurge

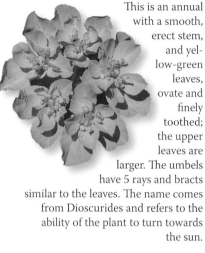

This is an annual with a smooth, erect stem, and yellow-green leaves, ovate and finely toothed; the upper leaves are larger. The umbels have 5 rays and bracts similar to the leaves. The name comes from Dioscurides and refers to the ability of the plant to turn towards the sun.

Distributed | 10-50cm ↑ | ⛰ ⚓ ☠

| 1 | 2 | 3 | 4 | 5 | 6 | 7 | 8 | 9 | 10 | 11 | 12 |

Euphorbia myrsinites L.

EUPHORBIACEAE

Broad-leaved glaucous spurge

A perennial plant, very often spreading and with numerous grey, overlapping and fleshy leaves, similar to those of the myrtle from which it takes its name. There are 5-12 umbels with golden-yellow flowers and bracts. Found in stony and infertile places.

Epirus | 10-30cm ↑→ | ⛰ ⚓ ☠

| 1 | 2 | 3 | 4 | 5 | 6 | 7 | 8 | 9 | 10 | 11 | 12 |

Euphorbia paralias L.
Sea spurge

The beautiful Greek name of this plant was given to it by Theophrastus, and accurately describes its preferred biotope of sandy beaches. It is a perennial, with a stout stem, branching from the root, often a strong russet colour. The leaves are numerous, along almost the whole length of the stems; they are grey, straight-lanceolate, the upper ones broader. The umbel is round with 6 rays at the most, and the umbels have concave, ovate bracts.

Distributed | 20-60cm ↑ | ▲ ✦ ☠ | 1 2 3 4 5 6 7 8 9 10 11 12

Ricinus communis L.
Castor oil plant

A perennial plant with an erect stem and palm-lobed leaves, often russet-coloured with toothed lanceolate lobes. The clusters of hairy, red balls are in reality curious flower-spikes of female flowers without petals. The male flowers are found in the lower part of the spike and have many yellow stamens. Dioscurides named it *króton* (the ancient Greek word for 'tick') because the seed resembles an animal tick. The seeds are rich in oil (ricinus) which is used for manufacturing and pharmaceutical purposes. *R. communis* is often cultivated in gardens as a decorative plant and it is believed to repel insects. It is self-sowing, often on roadsides and in ravines.

Distributed | Up to 4m ↑ | ▲ ✦ ♣ ☠ ▮ ✿ | 1 2 3 4 5 6 7 8 9 10 11 12

FAGACEAE

Quercus

The oaks are polymorphic, trees or bushes, evergreen or deciduous; they are very useful both for their wood which is particularly hard, and for their fruits, the oak-galls, which were used in the past in the tanning process. There are more than ten different species found in Greece, and many hybrids with various forms which pose a problem where classification is concerned.

Quercus coccifera L.

FAGACEAE

Kermes oak

This is the most dominant species of oak and can last for a long time as a bush, taking various forms as a defense against grazing goats. When it has acquired a safe height, it becomes a tree and can exceed 15 metres. In its tree form, it was once considered to constitute a separate species (*Q. calliprinos*). Kermococcus vermillio, a beetle with scales that produce a red colouring (known as crimson) develops on its leaves, which are small, spiny, and of a lighter colour on the underside. This gives the tree its name.

Distributed | 1-15m ↑ |

| 1 | 2 | 3 | 4 | 5 | 6 | 7 | 8 | 9 | 10 | 11 | 12 |

Quercus ilex L.

FAGACEAE

Holm oak

This is a beautiful, evergreen tree which can reach a height of 20 metres. Its leaves are up to 7cm in length and are leathery with a small stalk, elliptical-lanceolate with little or no toothing at the lips; the latter more or less differentiates them from the other species. The acorn cups are small and hemispherical, covering the acorns only up to the middle. The trees often form small forests. The *smilax* referred to by Theophrastus is probably the same tree.

Distributed | Up to 20m ↑ |

| 1 | 2 | 3 | 4 | 5 | 6 | 7 | 8 | 9 | 10 | 11 | 12 |

GENTIANACEAE

Centaurium erythraea RAFN
Common centaury

The spikes of numerous pink flowers do not permit this beautiful plant to go unnoticed. It has quadrangular stems, erect and much-branched, and unlobed leaves, the lower ones being larger and arranged in a rosette. The flowers have 5 petals which are joined at the base. In times past it was used as a febrifuge. Found in rocky locations, on slopes and roadsides.

C. pulchellum generally resembles C. erythraea but it is smaller, and without a rosette of leaves at the base. It has looser flower-spikes, sometimes with white flowers.

Distributed | 10-50cm ↑ | 🏔 ⚓ ⚘ | 1 | 2 | 3 | 4 | 5 | 6 | 7 | 8 | 9 | 10 | 11 | 12 |

GERANIACEAE

Erodium gruinum (L.) L'HER
Long-beaked heronsbill or storksbill

The erodia, like the geraniums which they resemble, took their name from the characteristic fruit with its long beak which recalls that of a heron. *E. gruinum* is an annual, hairy plant with three-lobed, toothed leaves. The flowers are on a very long flower-stalk, with violet petals which fall a few hours after blooming. Found in stony places.

Distributed | 20-40cm ↑ | 🏔 ⚓ | 1 | 2 | 3 | 4 | 5 | 6 | 7 | 8 | 9 | 10 | 11 | 12 |

Geranium

The fruits produced by the species of this genus resemble the bill of the crane in shape, hence their name. The flowers have 5 sepals, 5 petals and 10 stamens. More than 20 species are found in Greece, with many of them so small that they go unnoticed; *G. robertianum* is one of the latter.

Geranium macrorrhizum L.

GERANIACEAE

Geranium macrorrhizum

Perhaps the most beautiful of all the geraniums. This is a perennial, hairy and much-branched, with large, pink flowers in terminal inflorescences. The sepals are hairy and russet-coloured. The stamens are pink and long. The leaves are palm-lobed and toothed. Found in forest woodland and in rocky locations in northern Greece.

Macedonia, Thrace, Epirus, Thessaly, Sterea | 10-30cm ↑ | 🔺 ⬇ ◆ | 1 2 3 4 5 6 7 8 9 10 11 12

Geranium sanguineum L.

GERANIACEAE

Bloody cranesbill

A perennial, hairy plant with deeply-cut, sharply-pointed leaves. It has large flowers which are pink and up to 3cm in diameter, with short stamens and petals double the size of the sepals. It often grows in beautiful clumps. Found in dry locations.

Distributed | 10-40cm ↑ | 🔺 ⬇ | 1 2 3 4 5 6 7 8 9 10 11 12

Geranium tuberosum L.

Tuberous cranesbill

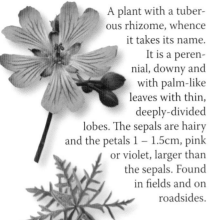

A plant with a tuberous rhizome, whence it takes its name. It is a perennial, downy and with palm-like leaves with thin, deeply-divided lobes. The sepals are hairy and the petals 1 – 1.5cm, pink or violet, larger than the sepals. Found in fields and on roadsides.

Distributed | 10-40cm ↑ | 🏔 ⚘ | 1 2 3 4 5 6 7 8 9 10 11 12

GESNERIACEAE

Haberlea rhodopensis FRIV.

Haberlea rhodopensis

This is endemic to the Balkans. A beautiful perennial plant, it is believed to be a remnant from the Ice Age, at least 2 million years old. The leaves are large, lanceolate, toothed and stalkless, arranged in rosettes at the base of one or more stems. There are 1 - 5 flowers on each stem, violet with light-coloured lips. The plant is resistant to drought, and prefers shady locations. It is a species protected by law, found in several areas of Greece and Bulgaria.

Thrace, Macedonia | 5-15cm ↑ | 🏔 ⚘ ⚘ ◆ | 1 2 3 4 5 6 7 8 9 10 11 12

Jankaea heldreichii Boiss.

Jankaea heldreichii

Jankaea, like its relative *Haberlea*, is also a remnant from the Ice Age. It has grey leaves, typically hairy, elliptical and arranged in rosettes. The flowers are violet, bell-like with long flower-stalks, and divided into 4 deep lobes. It is a rare plant and found only on Olympus up to a height of 1400 metres.

Olympos | Up to 10cm↑ |

| 1 | 2 | 3 | 4 | 5 | 6 | 7 | 8 | 9 | 10 | 11 | 12 |

GLOBULARIACEAE

Globularia alypum L.

Shrubby globularia

An evergreen, densely-branched shrub with oblong-lanceolate leaves, entire or with a few shallow lobes, distributed along the whole length of the stem. The flower-bearing heads are hemispherical, with a diameter of up to 3cm and toothed florets, blue-violet in colour. This is an aromatic plant with purgative properties. Found in dry, stony areas, phrygana and thickets.

Distributed | Up to 80cm↑ |

| 1 | 2 | 3 | 4 | 5 | 6 | 7 | 8 | 9 | 10 | 11 | 12 |

Hypericum

This is a polymorphic genus which includes herbaceous plants, phrygana and shrubs. The flowers are often in a wave-like arrangement and normally have 5 sepals, 5 petals – usually yellow – and many stamens. Generally, the flowers have a diameter of 2-3cm with the exception of *H. Olympicum* in which it can reach 5.5cm. More than 40 species and subspecies are found in Greece, a fair number of which are endemic, such as *H. empetrifolium* ssp. *tortuosum* which is a creeping hypericum with a woody stem, endemic to Crete.

Hypericum empetrifolium Willd.

Hypericum empetrifolium

The numerous, blindingly yellow flowers of this plant immediately distinguish it from the others. It has erect, russet-coloured stems and small, linear leaves which grow in tripartite whorls along the whole length of the stem. The petals are narrow, much longer than the sepals, and the stamens are in bunches, joined at the base. The plant is used in folk medicine as a healing agent. Found in thickets, on slopes, and in rocky locations.

Distributed | Up to 50cm↑ |

| 1 | 2 | 3 | 4 | 5 | 6 | 7 | 8 | 9 | 10 | 11 | 12 |

Hypericum perfoliatum L.

Hypericum perfoliatum

A plant with an erect stem which has two characteristic lines along its length. The leaves are lanceolate, smooth and opposite, with transparent stippling; their length can reach 6cm and they are periblastic, a characteristic which gives the name to this species. The flowers are yellow and up to 2.5cm in size, and the sharply-pointed sepals have black stippling. The stamens are of about the same length as the petals. Found in ditches and shady places.

Distributed | 20-40cm ↑ |

| 1 | 2 | 3 | 4 | 5 | 6 | 7 | 8 | 9 | 10 | 11 | 12 |

Hypericum perforatum L.   GUTTIFERAE
Perforate St. John's wort

This plant typically has black stippling on almost all its parts. It has an erect stem with two swollen lines along its length and elongated leaves, ovate and grey in colour, lighter on the underside. The leaves bear a multitude of transparent stipples which give them a perforated appearance – hence the name. The sepals are rather shorter than the petals. Found in fallow fields, dry and stony locations, and in phrygana.

Distributed | 10-50cm ↑ | | 1 2 3 4 5 6 7 8 9 10 11 12

● *Hypericum trichocaulon* Boiss. & Heldr.   GUTTIFERAE
Hypericum trichocaulon

A small, beautiful plant, endemic to the mountains of western Crete. It has many stems, erect or creeping, and elongated, ovate leaves with transparent black stippling. The flowers have petals that are deep red on the underside and sepals that are smaller, with black stippling. Found in stony locations, often in the shade of other plants.

Crete | 5-15cm ↑ | | 1 2 3 4 5 6 7 8 9 10 11 12

LABIATAE

This is a large family which includes phrygana or shrubs, usually aromatic due to the presence of glands on the leaves and stems which secrete essential oils. The pleasant aroma of the Greek countryside, especially during summer when the high temperatures assist in the sublimation of the oils, is due mainly to plants such as sages, oregano and lavender, which are all members of this family. Two other anatomical characteristics of the labiatae are the generally almost quadrangular cross-section of the stem and the zygomorphic form of the flower, i.e. its symmetry on a vertical axis. The flowers have two lips - more rarely one - hence the Latin *labiatae* and Greek name *hilanthí* from the words meaning 'lip'.

Acinos alpinus (L.) MOENCH. / syn. *Satureja alpina*   LABIATAE
Acinos alpinus

A small, herbaceous plant with branching stems, erect or prostrate. The leaves are usually unlobed, ovate-lanceolate, downy and with a small stalk. The small, funnel-shaped pink flowers grow from the leaf axils and have an oblong, hairy calyx with characteristic stripes. Found in stony locations in the mountain and alpine zone.

Distributed | 10-30cm ↑→ |

| 1 | 2 | 3 | 4 | 5 | 6 | 7 | 8 | 9 | 10 | 11 | 12 |

Ballota acetabulosa (L.) BENTHAM   LABIATAE
Garden horehound, false dittany

A phrygano plant which has many erect stems and is covered with dense, woolly down. The leaves are up to 5cm, ovate, opposite, and have a short stalk. The flowers are violet and arranged in whorls along the length of the stem with 6-12 in each whorl. A typical feature is constituted by the calyces, shaped like little cups, out of which the flowers grow; the calyces themselves continue to grow even after the flowers have fallen. In the past, the calyx was used as a lamp-wick. The practice was known from antiquity (Dioscurides used the word 'thryallída', meaning wick). The name of the plant comes from the Latin *acetabulum*' the word used by the Romans for the little container with which they measured vinegar. Found in sun-drenched, stony locations.

Peloponnese, Aegean, Crete, Evvia, Attica, Sterea | 10-60cm ↑ |

| 1 | 2 | 3 | 4 | 5 | 6 | 7 | 8 | 9 | 10 | 11 | 12 |

Ballota pseudodictamnus Benth.

LABIATAE

Ballota pseudodictamnus

Similar to B. acetabulosa
but with leaves up to 2cm
and very small flowers.
Theophrastus refers to it
as *díctamnon* but naturally
it has nothing to do with
the plant which is known
under that name today.
His 'pseudodíctam-
non' refers not to this
plant but to its relative,
B. acetabulosa. Found in
stony places.

Aegean, Crete | 20-50cm ↑ | 1 2 3 4 5 6 7 8 9 10 11 12

Lamium amplexicaule L.

LABIATAE

Henbit deadnettle

A delicate annual plant,
downy with an erect
stem and toothed,
kidney-shaped
leaves, the upper
ones periblastic and
overlapping or joined,
the lower ones on a long
stalk. The flowers are
whitish-pink with a
thin tube that is much
longer than the calyx.
The plant is common
in both cultivated and
fallow fields.

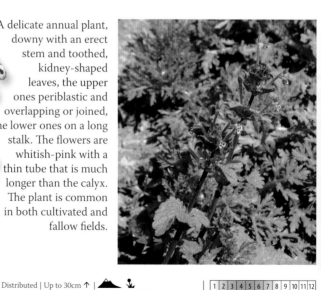

Distributed | Up to 30cm ↑ | 1 2 3 4 5 6 7 8 9 10 11 12

Lamium garganicum L.
Large red deadnettle

A perennial plant, much-branched; it can take the form of a bush. The leaves are heart-shaped, toothed and have a long stalk. The flowers are numerous with a tube much longer than the calyx; they are white, with pink linear markings and stipples. The upper lip is irregularly toothed, with a length the same as that of the tube. Found in the mountain and alpine zone, often beneath other plants.

Distributed | 10-40cm ↑ | ⌂ ◣ ▬

| 1 | 2 | 3 | 4 | 5 | 6 | 7 | 8 | 9 | 10 | 11 | 12 |

Lavandula stoechas L.
French lavender

The wild lavender is a much-branched phrygano plant, very aromatic with downy, linear leaves along the length of the stem. The flowers are small, funnel-shaped and dark violet in colour, arranged in a dense ear-like spike at the tip of which large rosy bracts develop, with a length of up to 5cm. This is a plant of pharmaceutical value which in folk medicine is used as a sedative. In former times, an oil was produced from it for use in various pharmaceutical and aromatic preparations. Found in thickets, phrygana and in stony locations.

Distributed | 30-100cm ↑ | ⌂ ◣ ▬ 🍶 ✿

| 1 | 2 | 3 | 4 | 5 | 6 | 7 | 8 | 9 | 10 | 11 | 12 |

Nepeta melissifolia LAM. LABIATAE
Nepeta melissifolia

A perennial plant with an erect, downy stem; the leaves have long stalks and are almost triangular, toothed and similar to those of the genus Melissa. The flowers are blue or violet with dark stippling and the calyx is short with stripes which reach to the middle of the tube. The flowers develop in whorls which all together form a loose, cone-like spike. Found in phrygana and in gorges.

Crete, Cyclades | 20-50cm ↑ | 🔺 ⚘ ◆

1 2 **3 4** 5 6 7 8 9 10 11 12

Origanum dictamnus L. LABIATAE
Cretan dittany

The fame of this little phrygano plant, which is endemic to Crete, assumed mythological proportions from antiquity onwards. Plutarch and also many other authors wrote about the *agrimi* (wild goat) which was wounded by the arrow of a hunter and ate dittany in order to heal itself, and the story was illustrated in art form during the Renaissance. Even today, dittany is considered to be a panacea for a number of ailments. Its collection from the usually inaccessible places in which it grows has cost the life of many, but also led to a significant decrease in the number of its populations. It is a much-branched plant with ovate leaves, covered in dense white down. The flowers are whitish-pink with many russet-coloured, overlapping bracts. Found on cliffs, in gorges and in rocky locations. It is no longer gathered on a large scale today; the dittany sold on the markets is a plant cultivated for that very purpose.

Crete | 5-40cm ↑ | 🔺 🌿 ⚱ 🏛 ◆ 🌱

1 2 3 4 5 **6 7 8 9** 10 11 12

Origanum microphyllum (Benth.) Vogel LABIATAE

Origanum microphyllum

A small, much-branched phrygano plant with the aroma of
lavender. It has thin, russet-
coloured stems and
little ovate, downy
leaves. The flowers
are small and pink-
ish-violet, arranged
in a small ear-like
spike, with bracts
covered with dense
white hairs. Found
on stony slopes and in phrygana
in the White Mountains of
Crete, and on Dikti.

Crete | 30cm ↑ |

1	2	3	4	5	6	7	8	9	10	11	12

Origanum onites L. LABIATAE

Pot marjoram

This phrygano plant has erect stems and downy, heart-shaped opposite
leaves along the whole length of the stem; the lower ones are stalked, the
upper ones stalkless. The flowers are white with large stamens in dense
corymbs. The plant is one form of common oregano which is collected along
with the other more or less similar form (*O. vulgare)* and used as a herb in cooking. Found
in stony places and on slopes. The name of the genus derives from the Greek words *oros*
(mountain) and *ganó* (to enjoy), while
its epithet 'onites' probably refers to
the similarity between the shape of the
flower buds and that
of pieces of don-
key dung (*onís=*
donkey in
ancient
Greek).

Sterea, Peloponnese, Aegean, Crete | 20-40cm ↑ |

1	2	3	4	5	6	7	8	9	10	11	12

Phlomis cretica C.Presl.
Phlomis cretica

LABIATAE

A downy, much-branched phrygano plant which does not exceed 50cm in height. The leaves are lanceolate with a velvet surface; the lower ones have longer leaf-stalks than the upper ones. The flowers are yellow, longer than the toothed and hairy calyces, in dense whorls. Found in dry, stony locations and phrygana.

Peloponnese, Aegean, Crete, Rhodes | Up to 50cm ↑ |

| 1 | 2 | 3 | 4 | 5 | 6 | 7 | 8 | 9 | 10 | 11 | 12 |

Phlomis fruticosa L.
Jerusalem sage

LABIATAE

A branching phrygano plant or shrub, similar to P. cretica but with a height which can reach to over 1 metre and leaves that are white on the underside, the lower ones stalked, the upper ones stalkless. The flowers are yellow, up to 4cm, with the upper lobe hairy, arranged in alternate whorls. Found in rocky places, in thickets and in phrygana.

Distributed | Up to 1,20m ↑ |

| 1 | 2 | 3 | 4 | 5 | 6 | 7 | 8 | 9 | 10 | 11 | 12 |

● *Phlomis lanata* WILLD.

Phlomis lanata

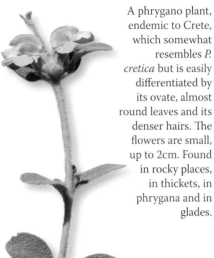

A phrygano plant, endemic to Crete, which somewhat resembles *P. cretica* but is easily differentiated by its ovate, almost round leaves and its denser hairs. The flowers are small, up to 2cm. Found in rocky places, in thickets, in phrygana and in glades.

Crete | 50cm ↑ |

| 1 | 2 | 3 | 4 | 5 | 6 | 7 | 8 | 9 | 10 | 11 | 12 |

Prasium majus L.

LABIATAE

Prasium

A perennial phrygano plant or small shrub with smooth, woody stems. The leaves are heart-shaped, smooth, toothed and grassy green in colour, with a little stalk. It is identified by its white flowers which are always in pairs, with bell-shaped calyces which are hairy on the inside. P. majus is a basic component of *hórta* – the mixture of wild greens which is known as *tsitsiristá*, used as a filling in *hortópites* (little pastry envelopes) or served as an accompaniment to meat dishes. It is usually found on rocky slopes.

Distributed | 20-80cm ↑ |

| 1 | 2 | 3 | 4 | 5 | 6 | 7 | 8 | 9 | 10 | 11 | 12 |

Rosmarinus officinalis L.

LABIATAE

Rosemary

A large, much-branched phrygano plant or bush with narrow, spiky leaves. Axillary flowers, white or blue, with characteristically large stamens. The plant is strongly aromatic and has may uses in the manufacture of pharmaceuticals and perfumes. The leaves are used as a herb in cookery. Rosemary is usually cultivated or self-sowing near to settlements.

Distributed | Up to 1,5m↑ | 〔1〕〔2〕〔3〕〔4〕〔5〕〔6〕〔7〕〔8〕〔9〕〔10〕〔11〕〔12〕

Salvia argentea L.

LABIATAE

Silver sage

More than 20 species of sage are found in Greece, most of which are aromatic. *S. argentea* has an erect, hairy stem, and large ovate leaves which have asymmetrical lobes and are covered in silvery hairs. The plant is considered to be a biennial, with the leaves developing in a large and impressive rosette in the first year and the flower-bearing stems in the second; it is a common phenomenon of the plant that it lives for a number of years. The flowers are white with pink hairs on the large and impressive upper lip, in a harmonious circular arrangement in alternate whorls. Found in stony locations and in fallow fields.

Epirus | 0,50-1m ↑ | 〔1〕〔2〕〔3〕〔4〕〔5〕〔6〕〔7〕〔8〕〔9〕〔10〕〔11〕〔12〕

Salvia pomifera L.

Salvia pomifera

A phrygano plant with slightly less down than S. argentea and with large wavy leaves, thinly toothed at the lip. The corolla is whitish-pink and in dense racemes, with calyces that are bell-shaped and continue to grow after the flowers have withered. This is a very aromatic plant which is often used as a tisane (tea). Found on rocky cliffs and slopes.

Sterea, Aegean, Crete | Up to 120cm ↑ | 🔺 🦫 🍶 🏵 | 1 2 3 4 5 6 7 8 9 10 11 12

Salvia sclarea L.

Clary

This is a plant with a very downy stem and stalked leaves which are heart-shaped and of a size that can reach to 10cm. The large, white, leaf-like bracts with the pink shading at the lips are very characteristic. The flowers are arranged in alternate whorls which form a large, elongated spike. An aromatic and medicinal plant common, in barren locations.

Macedonia, Epirus | 40-80cm ↑ | 🔺 ⚓ 🍶 🏵 | 1 2 3 4 5 6 7 8 9 10 11 12

Salvia triloba L. / syn. *Salvia fruticosa*   LABIATAE
Three-lobed sage

A perennial phrygano plant with many stems, erect and covered with dense white down, sticky at the tip. The leaves are green on the surface and whitish on the underside with two small lobe-like leaflets at the base, a characteristic which gives the plant its name ('triloba' means 'three-lobed'). The flowers are light pink with toothed calyces that are sharply pointed and russet-coloured and cease their development after flowering. This is a very aromatic plant which is frequently used in tisanes. Found in stony locations and in phrygana.

Crete, Aegean | 40-80cm ↑ | ▲ ▬ ◆ ⬗ ▮ | 1 2 3 4 5 6 7 8 9 10 11 12

Salvia verbenaca L.   LABIATAE
Wild clary

This is a perennial with a thin stem, markedly quadrangular, and slightly hairy. The leaves are large and wing-lobed; those at the base have a long stalk, and those on the stem are stalkless. The flowers are bluish-violet, in loosely arranged whorls along the whole length of the stem. Small plants are often observed with densely arranged whorls. Found on roadsides and in stony locations.

Distributed | Up to 60cm ↑ | ▲ ↓ ▮ ⬗ | 1 2 3 4 5 6 7 8 9 10 11 12

Satureja thymbra L.
Summer savory

This is a small phrygano plant, much-branched and loosely covered with white hairs, with a scent similar to that of thyme. It has inverted ovate leaves, pointed and with 'eyelashes' near the base. The flowers are light pink and arranged in whorls with calyces that are pointed and hairy. A very aromatic plant which is often used as a flavouring in meat dishes. Found in dry, stony locations and in phrygana.

Distributed | 10-30cm ↑ | 1 2 3 **4 5 6** 7 8 9 10 11 12

Stachys cretica L.
Mediterranean woundwort

A perennial, whitish-green coloured herbaceous plant with numerous strong stems, erect and covered with dense white hairs. The leaves are elongated, lanceolate and finely toothed, the lower ones stalked, the upper ones almost stalkless. The flowers are light pink and arranged in whorls at a fair distance from each other. Found in stony locations, phrygana, and on roadsides.

Distributed | 20-70cm ↑ | 1 2 **3 4 5 6** 7 8 9 10 11 12

Stachys spinosa L. LABIATAE
Spiny woundwort

This endemic, strongly spined phrygano plant has numerous much-branched and hairy stems and usually grows in a spherical shape. The leaves are elongated, downy, concave, and almost stalkless. The flowers are white or pink, often occurring singly with a toothed, sharply-pointed calyx. Found in phrygana, on slopes, and in rocky locations.

Crete, Cyclades, Karpathos | 20-60cm ↑ |

| 1 | 2 | 3 | 4 | 5 | 6 | 7 | 8 | 9 | 10 | 11 | 12 |

Stachys spruneri BOISS. LABIATAE
Stachys spruneri

A small, perennial phrygano plant with a very hairy stem. The leaves are lanceolate, toothed, spear-like, with denser hairs on the underside. The flowers are white with a pink blazon, arranged in adjoining whorls with toothed, very hairy calyces. Found in stony mountain locations.

Sterea, Attica | 20-40cm ↑ |

| 1 | 2 | 3 | 4 | 5 | 6 | 7 | 8 | 9 | 10 | 11 | 12 |

Teucrium divaricatum Sieber ex Heldr. / syn. *Teucrium graecum*   LABIATAE

Teucrium divaricatum

A perennial, branched phrygano plant with woody, delicately haired stems and ovate leaves that are toothed and have a wedge-shaped base. The calyx is reddish-brown, tubular, toothed and hairy. The flowers are pink with a hairy tube longer than the calyx. Particularly characteristic are the large stamens, and the strongly folded middle lobe of the lower lip. Found in rocky locations and on slopes.

Crete, Aegean | 20-50cm ↑ |

| 1 | 2 | 3 | 4 | 5 | 6 | 7 | 8 | 9 | 10 | 11 | 12 |

Thymus capitatus (L.) Hoff. & Link. / syn. *Coridothymus capitatus*   LABIATAE

Thymus capitatus

This is the most common but at the same time most important of all the thymes, since it is responsible for the production of the best honey in the world. It forms small, much-branched and head-shaped bushes, which during the flowering period are bathed in pink, due to the flowers which form cone-shaped heads. The very large stamens are typical, as are the 'eyelashes' at the bases of the leaves. Found in dry, stony locations and in phrygana.

Distributed | 10-30cm ↑ |

| 1 | 2 | 3 | 4 | 5 | 6 | 7 | 8 | 9 | 10 | 11 | 12 |

Thymus leucotrichus HALÁCSY

Thymus leucotrichus

A small plant, covered in white hairs – hence its name. The leaves are lanceolate and the flowers whitish–pink, arranged in small heads. A very beautiful plant which prefers stony locations and crevices in the rocks of the mountain and alpine zone.

Peloponnese, Attica, Macedonia, Epirus | 10-20cm ↑ |

| 1 | 2 | 3 | 4 | 5 | 6 | 7 | 8 | 9 | 10 | 11 | 12 |

LAURACEAE

Laurus nobilis L.

Sweet bay

The plant occurs normally in bush form, but very often becomes a tree which can reach a good height. The leaves are distinguished by their numerous aromatic oil-bearing glands from which bay tree oil is distilled, to be used for pharmaceutical purposes and in perfumery. The symbolism of the bay tree is manifold; even today its branches are used for garlands and decoration at festivals. There are also 'more humble' uses of this noble plant, since the leaves are used as a flavouring in many dishes, especially those made with lentils.

Despite her beauty the nymph Daphne, daughter of the River Peneios, was not interested in relationships or love-affairs but preferred to hunt in the forests with Artemis. However, when one day the god Apollo came upon her and tried to seduce her, she changed into a tree. The god, unable to possess her, made a garland from the branches of the tree and set it on his head. From that time onwards, the bay tree was associated with the worship of Apollo. It became his sacred tree, providing his crown and the Delphic tripod, while the Pythia herself chewed bay leaves in order to be able to pronounce oracles.

Distributed | Up to 5m ↑ |

| 1 | 2 | 3 | 4 | 5 | 6 | 7 | 8 | 9 | 10 | 11 | 12 |

LEGUMINOSAE

This very large family which includes both small herbaceous plants and large trees, has certain particular characteristics which make its species easily recognizable. The name of the family is from the Latin 'legumen' and naturally refers to the shape of the pericarp, which here is that of a bean. Notably, beans, lentils and lupins are all examples of members of this large family. The leaves are composite, i.e. made up of many smaller leaflets, although this is a characteristic also met in other plants. Their flowers are usually zygomorphic with 5 petals in a butterfly-like arrangement (hence the name 'Psychanths') consisting of a main, (standard) petal, wings and a keel, as shown in the picture.

PETAL

WINGS

KEEL

Anagyris foetida L.
Bean trefoil

A shrub or tree which emits a strong, rank odour when shaken. The leaves are stalked and consist of three stalk-less leaflets. The flowers are yellow in axillary racemes, with calyces which are bell-shaped and toothed. The main (standard) petal is smaller than the elongated wings with black spots on its internal surface. Found in ditches, along hedges, and in thickets.

Distributed | 1-4m ↑ |

| 1 | 2 | 3 | 4 | 5 | 6 | 7 | 8 | 9 | 10 | 11 | 12 |

Anthyllis tetraphylla L. / syn. *Tripodion tetraphyllum*
Bladder vetch

LEGUMINOSAE

An annual, normally creeping herbaceous plant with leaves consisting of 3-5 leaflets, that of the tip being much larger than the others. The flowers grow in the leaf axils with a whitish-yellow main (standard) petal, larger than the yellow wings. The calyx is downy, swollen and yellow-green with russet stripes. Found at the edges of fields and in phrygana.

Distributed | Up to 40cm → |

| 1 | 2 | 3 | 4 | 5 | 6 | 7 | 8 | 9 | 10 | 11 | 12 |

Anthyllis vulneraria L.
Kidney vetch

A hairy, erect or creeping herbaceous plant with polymorphic leaves. The lower leaves consist of unevenly-sized leaflets with the central one much larger, while the upper leaves are more or less of the same size. The flowers are whitish-pink with the heads surrounded by leaf-like bracts and swollen calyces, which are very hairy. A polymorphic plant with many sub-species, and considered to have healing properties - hence its name. It is common in fields and on roadsides.

Distributed | More than 40cm ↑ |

| 1 | 2 | 3 | 4 | 5 | 6 | 7 | 8 | 9 | 10 | 11 | 12 |

Astragalus angustifolius LAM.
Astragalus angustifolius

LEGUMINOSAE

A spiny phrygano plant which grows in beautiful semicircular masses. The formation of some bushes into this shape is not a matter of chance. The spiny stems, intricately branching, protect the plant from grazing animals, wind and snow, while retaining shade and moisture through the summer period. *A. angustifolius* is one of the many types of astragalus found in Greece; it has spiny leaves with many pairs of narrow leaflets. The flower is white with a large standard petal, and wings and a keel which are much smaller, the latter with violet shading. Found in stony locations in the mountain and alpine zone.

Distributed | Up to 60cm ↑ |

| 1 | 2 | 3 | 4 | 5 | 6 | 7 | 8 | 9 | 10 | 11 | 12 |

Calicotome villosa (Poir.) Link
Spiny broom

LEGUMINOSAE

A common sight in the Greek countryside – the brilliant yellow slopes covered in broom and bathed in the scent of this beautiful plant. It is branching, very spiny and downy, with typical grooves along the length of the stems. The leaves have ovate leaflets, downy on the underside. The flowers are yellow, often in groups in the axils of the branches. The name of the genus derives from the Greek words *calyx* and *tomi* (cut) and refers to the way that the calyx splits obliquely during the development of the flower. Found in hedges, in thickets and in phrygana.

Distributed | Up to 2m ↑ | 🏔 ⛰

1	2	3	4	5	6	7	8	9	10	11	12

Ceratonia siliqua C.
Carob or locust tree

LEGUMINOSAE

This beautiful tree was cultivated in bygone days for its fruits, the well-known carobs, whose seeds were once used (although not as much today) in the production of cellulose and the pod for the production of an aerated beverage or for animal feed. The size of the seed is always the same and was used to define a unit of weight for gold – the 'carat'. The flowers are very small and develop in long racemes. The leaves have ovate leaflets, and are smooth and leathery. The plant has a scattered distribution but is very common on Crete, in the Peloponnese and in the islands.

Distributed | Up to 10m ↑ | 🏔 🌳 🏺 📖 ❧

1	2	3	4	5	6	7	8	9	10	11	12

Cercis siliquastrum L. LEGUMINOSAE
Judas tree

This beautiful tree with very decorative flowers is connected with Judas; according to tradition, he was hanged on such a tree after the betrayal. The flowers, like the calyx, are pink and develop in racemes directly from the branches. The smooth, kidney-shaped leaves follow the flowering and, when the hanging pods appear, take on a dull appearance. It is often cultivated as a decorative plant.

Distributed | Up to 5m ↑ | 　　　　　 1 2 **3 4** 5 6 7 8 9 10 11 12

• *Coronilla globosa* Lam. / syn. *Securigera globosa* LEGUMINOSAE
Coronilla globosa

A perennial shrub, endemic to Crete. The leaves have more than 10 ovate, elongated and smooth leaflets. The flowers are numerous and arranged in spherical heads with a diameter of up to 6cm. The petals are white, the main (standard) petal with pink veining, the keel with pink shading. Found on the sides of gorges, on slopes and in cool, shady locations.

Crete | Up to 1,5m ↑ | 　　　　　 1 2 3 **4 5 6 7** 8 9 10 11 12

Coronilla varia L.
Crown vetch

A perennial shrub with erect stems, herbaceous, smooth and with leaves resembling those of *C. globosa*. There are up to 20 flowers, whitish-pink with long flower-stalks in beautiful round heads; the name refers to the many varieties of shading. Found in both cultivated and unculti-vated fields and is often grown in gardens.

Epirus | 20-120cm ↑ | 🏔 🌱 🌿   1 2 3 4 5 6 7 8 9 10 11 12

Ebenus cretica L.
Cretan ebony

Despite its name, this impres-sive shrub which is only found on Crete bears no relation to the tropical tree of the same name. The leaves usually consist of three elongated ovate, hairy leaflets; more rarely there are five. The pink flowers have eyelash-like, hairy bracts at their base and form pyramidal spikes. Found on hillsides, often in large populations which present an impressive picture.

Crete | Up to 100cm ↑ | 🏔 🌑   1 2 3 4 5 6 7 8 9 10 11 12

Genista acanthoclada DC.

LEGUMINOSAE

Genista acanthoclada

A much-branching, cushion-shaped shrub with wand-like stems, very spiny, hence the name acanthoclada derived from the Greek words *ákantha* (spine) and *kládos* (branch). The leaves are small and stalkless, consisting of three lanceolate, elongated leaflets, which develop at the points where the stems branch. There are racemes of slightly downy flowers at the ends of the stems. For many years, these plants constituted the main source of combustible material for villages. Found in thickets, in phrygana and in downgraded areas.

Sterea, Peloponnese, Attica, Aegean, Crete | Up to 1,50m ↑ |

| 1 | 2 | 3 | 4 | 5 | 6 | 7 | 8 | 9 | 10 | 11 | 12 |

Lupinus albus L.

LEGUMINOSAE

White lupin

It is usually on the edges of fields that complete stands of these beautiful plants with their blue and more rarely white flowers can be seen; they are often the remnants of former cultivation. The lupins are edible and even today their yellow fruits are found on every dinner table during the Lenten period of fasting. *L. albus* is an annual plant; its leaves, like those of all the lupins, are arranged in a ray-like order, elliptic and hairy on the underside. The flowers are white with a short flower-stalk, alternate or in pairs in short racemes. The calyces have lips of equal length. The lupin is self-sowing near areas where it is already being grown.

Distributed | 50-100cm ↑ |

| 1 | 2 | 3 | 4 | 5 | 6 | 7 | 8 | 9 | 10 | 11 | 12 |

Lupinus angustifolius L.

LEGUMINOSAE

Narrow-leaved lupin

An annual plant, erect and with leaves that have 5-9 characteristic, narrow leaflets, hairy on the underside. The flowers are a beautiful blue in colour, alternate, with short flower-stalks and in a long raceme. The lower lip of the calyx is larger than the upper one, which is deeply bilobate. Found in phrygana, in thickets and in fields.

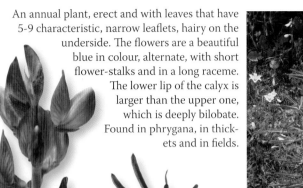

Distributed | 20-60cm ↑ | 1 2 3 **4 5 6 7** 8 9 10 11 12

Lupinus pilosus L.

LEGUMINOSAE

Lupinus pilosus

An annual plant, hairy and erect. The leaves have 7-11 oblong-lanceolate leaflets which are hairy on both sides. The flowers are blue with white brush-strokes and arranged in whorls along the whole length of the short raceme. The lower lip of the calyx is larger than the upper one. Found on slopes, in stony locations, in olive groves, and in ditches.

Aegean, Crete | 10-40cm ↑ | 1 2 **3 4** 5 6 7 8 9 10 11 12

Medicago arborea L.
Tree medick

This common plant was brought to Greece by the Medes during the period of the Persian Wars. Most of the medicago genus are herbaceous plants but tree medick can exceed 4 metres in height. It has trefoil leaves, as do all of the members of the genus, which are slightly toothed at the tip. The flowers are yellow and in clusters and the pods have a characteristic spiral form. Found in dry, stony locations. The plant is often cultivated for animal feed and also for decoration, particularly along the edges of roads.

Peloponnese, Crete, Aegean, Attica | 1-4m ↑

| 1 | 2 | 3 | 4 | 5 | 6 | 7 | 8 | 9 | 10 | 11 | 12 |

Medicago marina L.
Sea medick

A perennial, creeping plant, covered in dense silver hairs. The leaves have three leaflets, wedge-shaped and very hairy. The flowers are yellow with the standard petal larger than the keel, in little racemes. The pods are spiral in shape with two or three twists. The plant prefers sandy locations near the sea, where it forms little thickets.

Distributed | 10-50cm ↑→ |

| 1 | 2 | 3 | 4 | 5 | 6 | 7 | 8 | 9 | 10 | 11 | 12 |

Onobrychis ebenoides Boiss. & Sprun.

LEGUMINOSAE

Onobrychis ebenoides

Like many other hylanths, onobrychis is attractive to animals and the name of the genus refers to the donkey, which reacts to the sight of the plant by braying. *O. ebenoides* has many branches and leaves consisting of 9-15 narrow, downy, grey-green leaflets. The flowers are arranged in a spike, very similar to that of *Ebenus cretica*. The pods are spiny. Found in stony locations in the semi-mountainous zone.

O. sphaciotica, a beautiful plant with pink flowers which finds refuge on rocky slopes, is one of the rarest plants in Greece with a very limited distribution in the White Mountains.

Epirus, Peloponnese | 10-60cm ↑ |

| 1 | 2 | 3 | 4 | 5 | 6 | 7 | 8 | 9 | 10 | 11 | 12 |

Ononis spinosa L.

LEGUMINOSAE

Restharrow

A branching, phrygano plant with many spiny stems and leaves with ovate, toothed leaflets. The flowers are whitish–pink and larger than 1.5cm, with the standard petal larger than the keel. The calyx is hairy, toothed, and has pointed tips. Found in stony locations.

O. reclinata is a hairy plant, smaller ▶ and prostrate. It has similar flowers and prefers stony locations near the sea.

Distributed | 10-80cm ↑ |

| 1 | 2 | 3 | 4 | 5 | 6 | 7 | 8 | 9 | 10 | 11 | 12 |

Psoralea bituminosa L. / syn. *Bituminaria bitominosa* LEGUMINOSAE
Bitumen pea

A polymorphic plant which oftern forms dense stands along the sides of roads. The stem is slender, erect and has leaves with three elongated, lanceolate and long-stalked leaflets. The flowers are blue-violet with hairy calyces in almost round heads which have a very long flower stalk and grow in the axils of the leaves. The plant is easily recognised by the characteristic smell of tar which it emits. Common on roadsides, in ditches and in fallow fields.

Distributed | 0,20 - 1m ↑ | 　 1 2 3 4 5 6 7 8 9 10 11 12

Spartium junceum L. LEGUMINOSAE
Spanish broom

This shrub, which often embellishes the roadsides with its pleasantly-scented yellow flowers, has many long, thin stems and a few small, insignificant leaves. The flowers are arranged in racemes at the ends of the stems and produce flat pods up to 8cm in length. The strong, pliable stems of the plant are still used today to produce brooms and rope. Found in thickets and phrygana, and often cultivated as a decorative plant along the sides of roads.

Distributed | Up to 3m ↑ | 　 1 2 3 4 5 6 7 8 9 10 11 12

Trifolium campestre SCHREB.

LEGUMINOSAE

Hop trefoil

The clovers or trefoils take their name from their leaves which consist of three leaflets. They are small, herbaceous plants with butterfly-shaped flowers in heads or spikes. *T. campestre* is one of the few trefoils with many, small gold-yellow flowers in characteristic round heads which have a diameter a little larger than 1cm; the flowers take on a coffee-colour as time progresses. Found along roadsides, in ditches, olive groves, and in stony locations.

Distributed | Up to 30cm ↑ |

| 1 | 2 | 3 | 4 | 5 | 6 | 7 | 8 | 9 | 10 | 11 | 12 |

Trifolium purpureum LOIS.

LEGUMINOSAE

Purple clover

A tall plant with a hairy stem and leaves with narrow, almost linear leaflets. The flowers are purple with a length of more than 2cm, in a dense spike. The lower flowers are the first to open. The calyx is very hairy, and five-lobed – as are all of the trefoils – with linear lobes. Found in dry locations and in fields.

◄ *T. angustifolium* is similar, but smaller in size and its flowers open simultaneously.

Thrace, Macedonia, Epirus, Thessaly, Sterea, Peloponnese | 20-60cm ↑ |

| 1 | 2 | 3 | 4 | 5 | 6 | 7 | 8 | 9 | 10 | 11 | 12 |

Trifolium repens L.

White clover

A perennial, usually creeping, and hairless. The leaflets have a very short stalk, and are elliptic in shape with a circular white blazon at the base and dark, irregular lines along the length of the central vein. The flower-bearing heads have long flower-stalks with flowers of up to 1cm, whitish-pink in colour. Found in fields, cool locations and in phrygana.

Distributed | 10-30cm → | 🔺 ⚓

| 1 | 2 | 3 | 4 | 5 | 6 | 7 | 8 | 9 | 10 | 11 | 12 |

Trifolium stellatum L.

Star clover

An annual plant, hairy and with leaflets that are inverse heart-shaped, the side leaflets almost white, with veins and edges that are grassy green. The flower-bearing heads are spherical on long flower-stalks, and the flowers are white with yellow or pinkish tones. The calyces are hairy, and red on ripening when they take a characteristic star-shaped form. Found in fields, stony locations, and in phrygana.

Distributed | 10-30cm ↑ | 🔺 ⚓

| 1 | 2 | 3 | 4 | 5 | 6 | 7 | 8 | 9 | 10 | 11 | 12 |

Trifolium uniflorum L.

Trifolium uniflorum

A beautiful, perennial, usually with a creeping habit, and leaves on long stalks. The leaflets are toothed, often with a white blazon. The flowers are white or whitish-pink, solitary and on long flower-stalks which grow in the axils of the lower leaves. The calyx is tubular. Found in phrygana, on slopes, and in dry, stony locations.

Distributed | 10-20cm ↑→ | 🔺 ↓ | 1 2 3 4 5 6 7 8 9 10 11 12

Vicia pinetorum Boiss. & Sprun.

Vicia pinetorum

A well-populated genus which includes the species *V. faba*, the well-known broad bean. *V. pinetorum* is a beautiful endemic plant of central Greece; it is a perennial and climbs with the help of its branching tendrils. The leaves consist of more than 10 pairs of elliptic leaflets. The flowers are white and in dense, elongated racemes. It prefers shady, forest locations in the mountain zone.

Sterea, Attica, Evvia | 50-100cm ↑ | 🔺 🌿 ◆ | 1 2 3 4 5 6 7 8 9 10 11 12

Linum arboreum L.
Tree flax

This is a small shrub with a woody stem and fleshy leaves. The basal leaves develop into a rosette and are spatulate with a length of up to 3cm, while the upper leaves are smaller and lanceolate. The flowers have 5 petals up to 3cm in length, much longer than the sepals, and are arranged in terminal racemes. It is normally found on the rocky slopes of gorges.

Crete, Rhodes, Aegean | 20-40cm ↑ |

| 1 | 2 | 3 | 4 | 5 | 6 | 7 | 8 | 9 | 10 | 11 | 12 |

Linum bienne MILL. / syn. *Linum angustifolium*
Pale flax

A plant of slender growth, with many erect stems and narrow leaves that are lanceolate and alternate along the whole length of the stem. The flowers are light-coloured, blue-violet with dark veins, and the sepals smaller and spiky. The plant resembles *L. usitatissimum*, the cultivated flax which is much larger in size. Found in fields, phrygana, and olive groves.

Distributed | 20-50cm ↑ |

| 1 | 2 | 3 | 4 | 5 | 6 | 7 | 8 | 9 | 10 | 11 | 12 |

Linum elegans Sprun.

LINACEAE

Linum elegans

This is a beautiful plant with many short stems and lower leaves up to 2cm with a small stalk, arranged in a rosette. The upper leaves are stalkless, sharply pointed, and fluted. The flowers have yellow petals up to 2cm and the sepals are shorter and straight. Found in rocky locations, in the mountain and alpine zone.

Macedonia, Thessaly, Sterea, Attica, Peloponnese, Epirus, Evvia, Thrace | Up to 15cm ↑ | ▲ ↲ | 1 2 3 4 5 6 7 8 9 10 11 12

LORANTHACEAE

Viscum album L.

LORANTHACEAE

Mistletoe

An evergreen parasite with a preference for trees and in particular chestnut, pine and fir. The fruit is a round white berry whose sticky flesh was used in bygone days to make bird-lime, i.e to coat twigs used to entrap birds. The plant has had pharmaceutical uses since antiquity; Theophrastus believed it to be a remedy for epilepsy. The sticky fruit – the 'gue' of the Anglo-Saxons, is still used to decorate the doorways of houses at Christmas; this custom is a remnant of Druidic belief, while in Greek mythology Persephone used the plant to open the gates of Hades.

Distributed | 20-50cm ↑ → | ▲ ⬛ | 1 2 3 4 5 6 7 8 9 10 11 12

LYTHRACEAE

Lythrum junceum Banks & Sol.
Lythrum junceum

A perennial plant with erect quadrangular stems. The leaves are elongated, stalkless, the lower ones opposite, the upper ones alternate and more densely arranged. The flowers are pink with a light-coloured throat, growing singly in the leaf axils. It is common along streams, the banks of rivers and in damp locations generally, often in dense stands.

Distributed | 20-70cm ↑ |

| 1 | 2 | 3 | 4 | 5 | 6 | 7 | 8 | 9 | 10 | 11 | 12 |

MALVACEAE

Alcea pallida (Willd.) Waldst. & Kit.
Alcea pallida

An impressive plant with a strong stem, erect and with a height that can exceed 2 metres. The leaves are large, hairy, and kidney-shaped with shallow lobes. The flowers are up to 8cm, pink or purple with a very short flower-stalk. The plant is common in hedges and on the sides of roads.

A. rosea (the hollyhock) is similar, found in gardens and widely cultivated as a decorative plant.

Distributed | 1-2.5m ↑ |

| 1 | 2 | 3 | 4 | 5 | 6 | 7 | 8 | 9 | 10 | 11 | 12 |

Lavatera bryoniifolia Mill.

MALVACEAE

Lavatera bryoniifolia

A plant with many slender, tall branches. The leaves are palmately lobed, hairy and stalked, similar to those of the bryony, whence it takes its name. The flowers are pink with a diameter that can reach 4cm and in a loose arrangement, along almost the whole length of the stem. Normally found on roadsides and in dry locations.

Peloponnese, Aegean, Rhodes, Crete, Attica, Sterea, Evvia | Up to 2m ↑ | 🔺 ↯ | 1 2 3 4 5 6 7 8 9 10 11 12

Lavatera cretica L.

MALVACEAE

Cretan mallow, Small tree mallow

A smaller plant than L. bryonifolia, with erect or spreading stems. The leaves are downy, the upper ones with five deep, toothed lobes, and the lower ones almost round. The flowers are pink with dark veining and grow in bunches in the leaf axils. Found on roadsides and in abandoned fields.

Distributed | 20-150cm ↑ | 🔺 ↯ | 1 2 3 4 5 6 7 8 9 10 11 12

Malva cretica Cav.

Malva cretica

This little mallow has hairy stems, erect or prostrate, and toothed leaves which vary in shape, the lower ones being almost rounded and the upper ones having very narrow lobes. The flowers have a diameter of up to 2cm and are light pink in colour with dark veining. A characteristic of the plant is the hypocalyx covered by the trilobate, pointed–tipped calyx that is twice its length. Found in barren, stony locations.

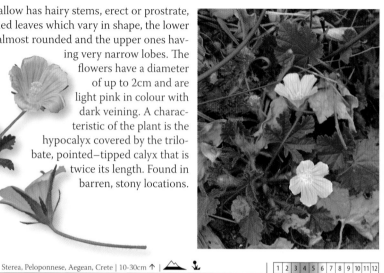

Sterea, Peloponnese, Aegean, Crete | 10-30cm ↑ |

| 1 | 2 | 3 | 4 | 5 | 6 | 7 | 8 | 9 | 10 | 11 | 12 |

Malva sylvestris L.

Common mallow

This is the most common of the mallows and the one which is mainly collected for pharmaceutical purposes. It is almost completely identical with *L. cretica* both in its leaves and flowers, but differs in the lobes of the calyx, which in this case are narrower. The plant can live for at least two years and is found in hedges, on roadsides, and in barren locations.

Distributed | 30-120cm ↑ |

| 1 | 2 | 3 | 4 | 5 | 6 | 7 | 8 | 9 | 10 | 11 | 12 |

MORACEAE

Ficus carica L.

MORACEAE

Fig

This is one of the most common trees to be found in the Greek countryside; it grows very easily and is even found in the walls of ruined buildings. It has large palmately lobed leaves which, when cut, exude a milky liquid like the other parts of the plant. The flowers are tiny and hidden within the pear-shaped receptacle which, when ripe, constitutes one of the sweetest fruits – the fig. The ancient Athenians prohibited the export of figs, because they were considered a valuable commodity whose consumption was to be limited only to those living within the confines of the city.

Distributed | 2-5m ↑ |

1 2 3 4 5 6 7 8 9 10 11 12

MYRTACEAE

Myrtus communis L.

MYRTACEAE

Myrtle

The myrtle is a beautiful, evergreen bush which can reach a height of 3 metres and take a tree-like form. The leaves are opposite, elliptic, sharply pointed and very aromatic, since they have glands which produce essential oils. The flowers have 5 white petals, often with pink shading and typically with many stamens. The fruit is a berry, which becomes almost black during the ripening period. The plant is connected with Aphrodite. According to one myth the goddess used a twig of myrtle to cover her nakedness, when she rose out of the sea.

Distributed | 1-4m ↑ |

1 2 3 4 5 6 7 8 9 10 11 12

Olea europaea L.

OLEACEAE

Olive

According to mythology, Athena beat Poseidon in a contest to decide who would be the pa-tron-protector of Athens by planting an olive tree; at the ancient Olympic Games the victors were awarded only an olive branch. The cultivation of this blessed tree began in the Minoan period and has continued unbroken to the present day, at the same time providing us with a mass of symbolism. The olive is probably the most representative tree of the Medi-terranean area. There are huge tracts of olive groves in Greece, especially on Crete, in the Peloponnese, islands and mainland. The tree lives for a great number of years and it is not a rare phenomenon in very old trees for only the bark to have remained and the tree to have continued putting out lateral shoots. The value of the olive and its oil has been ascertained in recent years through the famous 'Seven Countries Study' which has shown conclusively that a Mediterranean regime of nutri-tion based on olive oil can reduce heart disease to a large degree.

Distributed | Up to 30m ↑ | 1 2 3 4 5 6 7 8 9 10 11 12

Epilobium angustifolium L.

ONAGRACEAE

Epilobium angustifolium

A beautiful, perennial plant with a slender trunk which can grow to a great height. It has large, lanceolate leaves up to 15cm with a very characteristic peripheral vein running parallel to the edge of the undulating lips. The flowers have pink, cudgel-like petals and are arranged in large ear-like spikes on the upper half of the stem. The name comes from the Greek *epí+ lobós* and refers to the simultaneous presence of a flower and ovary. Found on the edges of forests in the mountain zone.

Thrace, Macedonia, Epirus, Thessaly | Up to 2m ↑ |

| 1 | 2 | 3 | 4 | 5 | 6 | 7 | 8 | 9 | 10 | 11 | 12 |

© Y.S.

Oxalis pes-caprae L.

OXALIDACEAE

Bermuda buttercup

This grassy weed with the brilliant yellow flowers which covers fields and olive groves from the beginning of spring onwards was only introduced to the Mediterranean area about 200 years ago. The leaves have a characteristic heart-shape which resemble a hoof (*pes-caprae* means goat's hoof) while the large, yellow flowers grow in umbels at the tips of the delicate stems. This is the most widely distributed of all the weeds and found normally in huge populations.

Distributed | Up to 40cm ↑ |

| 1 | 2 | 3 | 4 | 5 | 6 | 7 | 8 | 9 | 10 | 11 | 12 |

PAEONIACEAE

These are perhaps the most beautiful flowers to be found in the Greek countryside. With their large flowers – usually white or red – they embellish the slopes of the mountains, presenting a unique sight to those fortunate enough to come across them. The people of antiquity valued the medicinal properties of the plant, and it was for this reason that they gave it the name of Paeon, the god of physicians. In Greece, five species are found, of which *Paeonia parnassica* with its deep red flowers is found on Parnassos, *Paeonia clusii* with its white flowers is found on Crete and Karpathos, and *Paeonia rhodia*, also white-flowered, is found on Rhodes. The three latter species are endemic to Greece. *Paeonia mascula* is the most frequently occurring species, with flowers of a variety of shades from pink to white, depending on the locality in which it is growing.

Paeonia mascula

Paeonia rhodia

Paeonia parnassica

Paeonia clusii STERN & STEARN

PAEONIACEAE

Clusius's peony

One of the most beautiful peonies with brilliant white flowers, rarely pink, which can reach to a height of 12cm and have the scent of clove. The leaves are deeply cut, and smooth on both sides. Although it was discovered for the first time on Ida by Bellon, it is now only found in the White Mountains and on Dikti. In Sfakia it is called *Pseuthia* = 'the false one' because its flowers are so beautiful they almost look as if they are synthetic. In bygone days, Sfakian bridegrooms used to pin a peony in their lapels.

Paeonia rhodia, also endemic, is similar in appearance, and considered by some botanists to be a subspecies of *P. clusii.*

Crete, Karpathos | Up to 80cm ↑ | 1 2 3 4 5 6 7 8 9 10 11 12

Corydalis solida (L.) Clairv. / syn. *Corydalis densiflora*

Corydalis solida

These plants are distinguished by their zygomorphic flowers with the typical oblong spur. *C. solida* is a small plant with an erect stem and leaves that are deeply cut into three divisions; also characteristic are the toothed bracts. The flowers are pink or whitish-pink in a long, dense raceme. Found in forests and hedgerows.

Epirus | 10-20cm ↑ | 1 2 3 **4** 5 6 7 8 9 10 11 12

● *Corydalis uniflora* (Sieber) Nyman

Corydalis uniflora

This little plant which likes to hide among thorny bushes is endemic to Crete. It has slightly fleshy, opposite leaves. There is often only one flower, more rarely 2-3; the flower is white with pink blazons on the petals. Found in rocky locations in the alpine and sub-alpine zone.

Crete | 10-15cm ↑ | 1 2 3 4 **5 6 7** 8 9 10 11 12

Fumaria capreolata L.
Ramping fumitory

The fumariae took their name from the aroma of smoke which they exude (*fumus* = smoke). *F. capreolata* has leaves divided into two or three segments, with sharply-pointed lobes. The flowers are white or pink with very dark lips. The two sepals are ovate, slightly toothed and a little broader than the tube. Found in barren locations and in fields.

Distributed | 20-100cm ↑ | 〽 ⚓

| 1 | 2 | 3 | 4 | 5 | 6 | 7 | 8 | 9 | 10 | 11 | 12 |

Fumaria officinalis L.
Common fumitory

This is a branching plant with very dissected leaves that have narrow lobes. The flowers are whitish-pink with dark lips and the upper petal ends in a long spur, as is the case in all the fumariae. The sepals are lanceolate, and narrower than the tube. Found in stony places.

Distributed | 20-100cm ↑ | 〽 ⚓ ▮

| 1 | 2 | 3 | 4 | 5 | 6 | 7 | 8 | 9 | 10 | 11 | 12 |

Glaucium flavum GRANTZ

Yellow horned poppy

A small, biennial shrub with fleshy, grey-coloured, palmately lobed leaves, the lower ones very large with a short stalk, the upper ones stalkless. It has impressive, gold-yellow flowers with 4 overlapping petals. The fruit is a slender, cylindrical capsule which can exceed 20cm in length. Found on roadsides, on slopes, on sandy beaches, and amidst rubble.

G. corniculatum ▶ (Red horned poppy) has winged-lobed leaves and red or orange flowers with a dark fleck at the centre.

Distributed | 30-80cm ↑ |

1 2 3 4 5 6 7 8 9 10 11 12

Papaver

The poppies, which in spring bathe the fields with their beautiful colour, are amongst the most loved wild flowers of the Greek countryside. Their leaves and stems are usually grey-green, while the flowers consist of two sepals which fall on flowering, and four petals which are normally red. A particular characteristic of poppies is the swollen capsule at the centre of the flower which contains the seeds, surrounded by many stamens. Around 10 species are found in Greece, all of them annual.

Papaver somniferum (Opium poppy)
This is the poppy from which opium is obtained through cuts in its spherical capsule. Cultivation is prohibited today.

Papaver argemone **ssp.** *nigrotinctum* (Fedde) Kadereit   PAPAVERACEAE
Papaver argemone ssp. nigrotinctum

This variety, found in Greece, is a subspecies which was once considered a separate species in itself. The leaves are deeply divided with elongated lobes, and lanceolate. The stems are slightly hairy. The plant has a small red or orange flower, dark at the centre. The capsule is elongated and hairy.

P. apulum is similar, but differs in the shape of the ▶ capsule - in this case that of an egg; it is also very bristly.

Aegean, Crete | 10-40cm ↑ | 1 2 3 4 5 6 7 8 9 10 11 12

Papaver purpureomarginatum Kadereit   PAPAVERACEAE
Papaver purpureomarginatum

This plant has winged-lobed leaves, the lobes toothed and lanceolate. The stems are slender and slightly hairy. The flower is relatively small, not larger than 4cm. The petals are light-coloured, tending towards orange, without black at the base. The capsule is smooth, small, and elongated, and the anthers are yellow.

P. dubium is similar, with flowers which can reach up to 6cm.

Peloponnese, Aegean, Crete | 10-40cm ↑ | 1 2 3 4 5 6 7 8 9 10 11 12

Papaver rhoeas L.

Common poppy, corn poppy

The most common poppy. The leaves are deeply divided and toothed. The flower-stalks are very bristly. The petals are large (2-3cm), brilliant red, and often with a black fleck at the base. The capsules are short, almost spherical, smooth, and surrounded by many stamens with black or brown anthers. Found in cultivated and fallow fields, olive groves etc. Very widely distributed.

 Distributed | 20-60cm ↑ |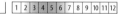

| 1 | 2 | 3 | 4 | 5 | 6 | 7 | 8 | 9 | 10 | 11 | 12 |

Phytolacca americana L.

American pokeweed

This plant originates from North America; it is self-sowing throughout Greece in fields, gardens and on roadsides. It has stems that are normally russet-coloured and large, lanceolate leaves which can reach a length of 30cm. The little white or pink flowers have only 5 sepals and grow in long racemes on stalks, opposite to the leaves. On ripening, the plant produces a fruit - a black berry - in very impressive bunches.

Distributed | Up to 3m ↑ |

| 1 | 2 | 3 | 4 | 5 | 6 | 7 | 8 | 9 | 10 | 11 | 12 |

Platanus orientalis L.

Oriental plane

This majestic, deciduous tree is well-loved in Greece and very often huge, ancient plane trees are to be found in village squares. It has large, palmately lobed leaves which are often toothed. The flowers grow in spherical spikes which hang on a long flower-stalk. The tree is connected with the kidnapping of Europa by the god Zeus, who had changed into a bull. The myth relates that the god took the beautiful young girl to Gortys and lay there with her under a plane tree which, from that time onwards, ceased to shed its leaves. Notwithstanding the myth, the plane tree at Gortys is of a particular evergreen, Cretan variety which is found sporadically all over the island. The tree prefers damp areas, the banks of rivers, streams and springs.

Distributed | Up to 20m ↑ |

| 1 | 2 | 3 | 4 | 5 | 6 | 7 | 8 | 9 | 10 | 11 | 12 |

Acantholimon androsaceum Boiss. / syn. *A. ulicinum, A. echinus*   PLUMBAGINACEAE

Acantholimon androsaceum

A perennial phrygano plant which forms hemispherical bushes in the sub-alpine and alpine zone. It has dense foliage, with linear leaves that are sharply pointed and give the plant a spiky appearance. The flowers are pink with five petals which, when they fall, reveal membranous calyces with dark red stripes; thus even when all the flowers have finished, the plant still has a beautiful appearance. It prefers open, rocky, limestone locations.

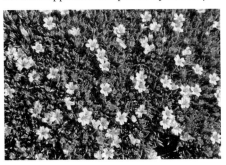

Peloponnese, Sterea, Aegean, Crete | Up to 20/60cm ↑→ | 1 2 3 4 5 6 7 8 9 10 11 12

Limonium sinuatum (L.) Mill.

Winged sea lavender

1 2 3 4 5 6 7 8 9 10 11 12

PLUMBAGINACEAE

The Limonia normally have slender, hard, branching stems and leaves concentrated at the base. Their flowers have a characteristic membranous calyx. They prefer seaside locations and many of them are endemic with a narrow distribution, such as *L. creticum* which is found in front of the caves at Matala and has been classified as 'vulnerable'. *L. sinuatum*, on the other hand, is a perennial with a wide distribution. It has winged leaves arranged in a rosette. The white flowers grow in dense corymbs and have a characteristic blue-violet, papery calyx. Also characteristic is the linear wing along the length of the stems.

L. creticum

Distributed | 20-40cm ↑→ | ⌂ ↓

POLYGALACEAE

Polygala venulosa Sm.
Milkwort

An herbaceous plant, with a much-branched stem and lanceolate, sharply-pointed leaves. The strange, zygomorphic, light blue flower consists of 5 unequal petals, 2 of which are atrophied, the lower one torn into a fringe. Likewise, of the 5 sepals two are very large and butterfly-shaped, with characteristic veining. It is believed that animals which graze on this plant produce more milk, a characteristic which has given the genus its name (*polygala* = much milk). Found in stony places, often amongst phrygana and bushes.

Attica, Evvia, Aegean, Crete, Peloponnese | Up to 30cm ↑→ | 🗻 ⚘

| 1 | 2 | 3 | 4 | 5 | 6 | 7 | 8 | 9 | 10 | 11 | 12 |

PORTULACACEAE

Portulaca oleracea L.
Purslane

An herbaceous plant, rather creeping, with branching stems and leaves that are inverse-ovate, fleshy and smooth, often with dark shading on the lips. The flowers are yellow and grow in the leaf axils or at the ends of the stems in small groups. It is used in salads and is commonly found in gardens and fields.

Distributed | Up to 50cm ↑→ | 🗻 ⚘ 🍳

| 1 | 2 | 3 | 4 | 5 | 6 | 7 | 8 | 9 | 10 | 11 | 12 |

Anagallis arvensis L.

Pimpernel

A small herbaceous plant, erect or prostrate with ovate-lanceolate, opposite leaves, stalkless and smooth. The orange-red or blue flowers grow on slender flower-stalks in the leaf axils. The edges of the petals bear little hairs which differentiate this species from the very similar *A. foemina*. Found in cultivated and fallow fields, ditches, and phrygana.

Distributed | 10-40cm ↑→ | ⛰ ⚓ ☠ ❦

| 1 | 2 | 3 | 4 | 5 | 6 | 7 | 8 | 9 | 10 | 11 | 12 |

Cyclamen

These are perennial herbaceous plants with a large tuber at the root from which the leaves and flowers grow on long stalks. The flowers are always white or pink, nodding, and have a very characteristic shape. The corolla is divided into five parts which are turned backwards in a spiral-like manner to cover the curved part of the flower-stalk. 5 species are found in Greece, some autumnal, and some appearing in spring.

C. persicum is found on the islands of the south-east Aegean. It is a very beautiful plant and the progenitor of the cultivated varieties. It has white or rose-pink flowers with deep pink on the corolla. It is relatively early-flowering, in various biotopes.

• *Cyclamen creticum* (Doerfl) Hildebr.

Cretan sowbread

The endemic Cretan cyclamen is pure white but can often be found with slight pink shading. It has a corolla without protuberances and leaves which resemble those of the ivy. Found in damp, shaded locations.

C. repandum is found in the Peloponnese and on Rhodes; it has pink flowers without corollary protuberances and there is no strong variation in the leaves. It is considered to be a species related to *C. creticum*.

Crete | 5-15cm ↑ | ⛰ ⚓ 🌱

| 1 | 2 | 3 | 4 | 5 | 6 | 7 | 8 | 9 | 10 | 11 | 12 |

Cyclamen graecum LINK

Greek sowbread

This has heart-shaped leaves with light-coloured markings, and red shading on the underside. The flowers are whitish-pink with dark pink lines and corollary protuberances; they appear in autumn. Found in stony locations.

Distributed | 5-15cm ↑ |

| 1 | 2 | 3 | 4 | 5 | 6 | 7 | 8 | 9 | 10 | 11 | 12 |

Cyclamen hederifolium AITON / syn. *Cyclamen neopolitanum*

Ivy-leaved Sowbread

This plant has leaves resembling those of the ivy (*hedera*) – hence the name. It has a very large, flattish tuber. The flowers are light pink, and with dark with corollary protuberances. It flowers in the autumn in cool, shady locations, and is commonly cultivated.

© Y. S.

Distributed | 5-10cm ↑ |

| 1 | 2 | 3 | 4 | 5 | 6 | 7 | 8 | 9 | 10 | 11 | 12 |

Lysimachia serpyllifolia SCHREB.

PRIMULACEAE

Lysimachia serpyllifolia

This little endemic plant has many stems and opposite leaves which are ovate and sharply pointed. The little yellow flowers have a diameter of 1–1.5cm, and are solitary, growing from the leaf axils. The fruits are small, spherical capsules which resemble the marbles that children use to play a game. The plant, which bears the name of the ancient physician Lysimachus of Kos, is found in stony locations in the mountain and alpine zone, often amongst other plants.

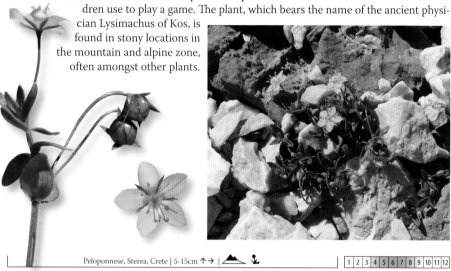

Peloponnese, Sterea, Crete | 5-15cm ↑ → | ▲ ⚓

| 1 | 2 | 3 | 4 | 5 | 6 | 7 | 8 | 9 | 10 | 11 | 12 |

Primula veris HUDS.

PRIMULACEAE

Spring cowslip

This is a perennial, smoothly downy plant with ovate, corrugated and stalked leaves. The flowers are yellow with orange dots on the inside, and very fragrant; they grow in a nodding umbel with a long flower-stalk. The cylindrical calyx is swollen in the middle and has 5 triangular, sharply-pointed lobes. Found in clearings and meadows in the mountain zone.

Macedonia, Epirus, Thessaly, Sterea, Peloponnese | 10-30cm ↑ | ▲ ⚓ ❀

| 1 | 2 | 3 | 4 | 5 | 6 | 7 | 8 | 9 | 10 | 11 | 12 |

Primula vulgaris Huds.

Primrose

The common primula is a very beautiful plant, almost without a stem and with inverse-ovate leaves that are corrugated, up to 15cm long, and very narrow at the base. The fragrant, whitish-yellow flowers are solitary, on a long flower-stalk, and have a diameter of up to 4cm. The downy calyx has 5 lanceolate, sharply-pointed lobes and reaches half-way up the tube. A very decorative plant, found in fields, meadows, clearings and damp locations.

Distributed | Up to 30cm ↑

| 1 | 2 | 3 | 4 | 5 | 6 | 7 | 8 | 9 | 10 | 11 | 12 |

PUNICACEAE

Punica granatum L.

Pomegranate

The pomegranate, mentioned in Homer, is a spiny tree with ovate, opposite, and leathery leaves. It produces beautiful, large very red flowers which form a round red fruit with a diameter that can be as much as 10cm – the pomegranate – containing hundreds of sweet, deep-red seeds. The skin of the pomegranate fruit is used as a natural dye and produces wonderful yellow-brown, earthy colours. Found in gardens, on the edges of fields, and in coppices.

Distributed | 2-7m ↑

| 1 | 2 | 3 | 4 | 5 | 6 | 7 | 8 | 9 | 10 | 11 | 12 |

Cytinus hypocistis L.
RAFFLESIACEAE

Cytinus

This peculiar, chlorophyll-free plant with its blindingly red colour grows as a parasite on the roots of ladania. It has red fleshy leaves that cover each other in succession. The flower has 4 petals, white or yellow, covered by the leaves, in dense heads, the outer flowers being male, the inner ones female. The name *hypocistis* originates from Dioscurides. Cytinus belongs to the same family as *Raflesia*, a tropical plant whose flower is the largest in the world with a diameter of 1 metre.

Distributed | 5-10cm ↑ |

| 1 | 2 | 3 | 4 | 5 | 6 | 7 | 8 | 9 | 10 | 11 | 12 |

Adonis annua L.
RANUNCULACEAE

Pheasant's eye

This plant has a smooth stem and wing-shaped leaves, torn and thread-like. The flowers are usually red, sometimes yellow and up to 2.5cm in diameter with 5 sepals and 6-10 petals which are dark at the base and thus form a black eye at the centre of the flower. The plant has medicinal properties and is found in stony locations, fields, olive groves, and vineyards.

Distributed | 10-40cm ↑ |

| 1 | 2 | 3 | 4 | 5 | 6 | 7 | 8 | 9 | 10 | 11 | 12 |

Adonis microcarpa DC.
Yellow pheasant's eye

An annual herbaceous plant with wing-shaped leaves, torn and thread-like. The flowers are yellow, with five sepals and 6-10 petals. Found in stony locations and fields.

A. cyllenea is a perennial plant with a height of 10-30cm; it has yellow flowers, and is endemic to Mount Kyllini (Zireia).

Aegean, Crete | 10-40cm ↑ |

| 1 | 2 | 3 | 4 | 5 | 6 | 7 | 8 | 9 | 10 | 11 | 12 |

Anemone

The anemones (or wild poppies) are perennials, herbaceous plants with certain particular characteristics that make them easy to recognize and differentiate from the poppies and ranunculi, with many of which they are confused. The anemones do not have petals, while the perianth consists of the sepals which have taken the place of petals. The leaves grow at the base of the stem, except for three smaller leaves which are situated in a whorl a little way below the flower. More than 6 species are found in Greece.

The name derives from the Greek word *ánemos*, meaning wind. One of the many attendant myths tells us about Anemone, a beautiful nymph who was a companion of Flora, the goddess of vegetation and had the misfortune to fall in love with her consort, Zephyros (the West Wind). When the goddess discovered the relationship, she drove away Anemone, who died of grief. However, Aphrodite transformed her into a flower which returns to life each spring until the wind blows its petals far away, ending its short life.

Anemone blanda SCHOTT & KOTSCHY
Mountain windflower

| 1 | 2 | 3 | 4 | 5 | 6 | 7 | 8 | 9 | 10 | 11 | 12 |

This beautiful anemone, which prefers clearings in mountain forests, is distinguished by the leaflets on the whorl which have a long stalk and are trilobate and toothed. The leaves at the base are similar, but larger. The flower has narrow sepals, many in number, which are blue-violet; the anthers are yellow. This is the mountain anemone of Theophrastus.

Thrace, Macedonia, Epirus, Thessaly, Sterea, Peloponnese, Evvia | 10-15cm ↑ |

Anemone coronaria L.

RANUNCULACEAE

Crown or poppy anemone

The most common anemone in the Greek countryside, and found in a multitude of forms and colours. The leaves of the whorl and base are deeply cut. The flowers are large, usually with five sepals, sometimes many more, with a length of up to 4cm and a number of blackish-mauve anthers. The colours of the sepals are numerous, most commonly red, white, violet, blue and pink. Their shape also varies, from round to pointed-tipped. The result is a multitude of varieties which often form a really polychrome carpet in olive groves and fields.

var. rosea

var. cyanea

var. phoenica

var. alba

Distributed | 20-30cm ↑ | 🏔 ⚓ ☠ 🌱

| 1 | 2 | 3 | 4 | 5 | 6 | 7 | 8 | 9 | 10 | 11 | 12 |

● *Anemone hortensis* ssp. *heldreichii* (Boiss.) Rech.   RANUNCULACEAE
Anemone hortensis

This plant is endemic to Crete and Karpathos. The leaves of the whorl are entire or trilobate, lanceolate, and the lower ones are deeply palmately lobed with strongly toothed lobes. The flower has many sepals, more than 10, which are white or pink and often blue at the base; the anthers are violet. Found in phrygana, olive groves, and stony places.

Crete, Karpathos | 15-45cm ↑ |

| 1 | 2 | 3 | 4 | 5 | 6 | 7 | 8 | 9 | 10 | 11 | 12 |

Anemone pavonina Lam.   RANUNCULACEAE
Peacock anemone

This plant resembles *A. hortensis*. It has 7-12 sepals, usually red with a white base, making it a very imposing flower. In southern Greece it is found with a pink or violet flower. The anthers are bluish-violet. Found in phrygana and fields.

Distributed, excluding Crete | 15-35cm ↑ |

| 1 | 2 | 3 | 4 | 5 | 6 | 7 | 8 | 9 | 10 | 11 | 12 |

Clematis cirrhosa L.

Virgin's bower

An evergreen, climbing bush with woody stems and smooth, saw-edged leaves. The five-part, bell-shaped whitish-yellow flowers grow on the stems from the previous year. This wild vine flowers in autumn and winter and often the flowers are so numerous that they cover the plant. On maturity, a multitude of fine hairs create the impression of a white comet. Found in hedgerows and in the zone of Mediterranean maquis.

Sterea, Attica, Peloponnese, Aegean, Crete | Up to 3m ↑ →

| 1 | 2 | 3 | 4 | 5 | 6 | 7 | 8 | 9 | 10 | 11 | 12 |

Clematis flammula L.

Fragrant clematis

This elegant climber has woody stems, russet-coloured on maturity, and composite leaves with ovate leaflets. The flowers are white with 4 narrow sepals and many stamens. The multitude of fragrant flowers makes the plant very decorative, and for this reason it is widely cultivated. Found in hedgerows and thickets.

Epirus | Up to 5m ↑

| 1 | 2 | 3 | 4 | 5 | 6 | 7 | 8 | 9 | 10 | 11 | 12 |

Consolida ajacis Schur. / syn. *Delphinium ajacis*

RANUNCULACEAE

Larkspur

This is an herbaceous plant with an erect, strong stem and very dissected leaves with narrow lobes. The zygomorphic blue or violet flowers have a long spur and grow in a long raceme. The blazon on the petals recalls the letter 'A'; according to mythology, the plant sprang from the blood of the Homeric hero Ajax when he killed himself. A decorative plant, found in both fields and gardens.

Epirus | 40-80cm ↑ | 🏔 ⚓ ☠ ❦

| 1 | 2 | 3 | 4 | 5 | 6 | 7 | 8 | 9 | 10 | 11 | 12 |

Delphinium staphisagria L.

RANUNCULACEAE

Delphinium

A hairy plant with a strong stem and height which often exceeds 1 metre. It has large, palmately lobed leaves, the lobes themselves either entire or trilobate, and sharply pointed. The azure or darker blue zygomorphic flowers are in a raceme at the end of the stem and distinguished by their characteristic, very short spur. The dust from the seeds has been used since antiquity to kill lice. Found in barren, stony places, fields and on roadsides.

Distributed | Up to 1m ↑ | 🏔 ⚓ ❚ ☠

| 1 | 2 | 3 | 4 | 5 | 6 | 7 | 8 | 9 | 10 | 11 | 12 |

Helleborus cyclophyllus Boiss.
Greek hellebore

This is a perennial plant with composite leaves and leaflets that are lanceolate and toothed, which look as if they are arranged in a circle. The yellowish-green, stalked and bell-shaped flowers with 5 sepals and a diameter of up to 5cm grow from the centre of the circle. This is both a poisonous and medicinal plant which was used from antiquity until recent times to treat psychological disorders. Found in clearings and shady, stony locations in the mountain zone.

Epirus | 30-50cm ↑ |

1	2	3	4	5	6	7	8	9	10	11	12

Nigella damascena L.
Love-in-a-mist, or Devil-in-a-bush

This herbaceous plant with the unusual flower has a slender, erect, and angular stem and very dissected leaves with thread-like lobes. The bracts of the flowers resemble the leaves – this is typical of the plant. The flower has 5 bluish-white sepals, many stamens and an ovary consisting partly of pockets with characteristically short 'beaks', which on maturity form a very swollen capsule. Found in fields, phrygana, olive groves, and on roadsides. It is cultivated as a decorative plant.

Distributed | 10-50cm ↑ |

1	2	3	4	5	6	7	8	9	10	11	12

Ranunculus asiaticus L.
Turban buttercup

The ranunculi occur in many forms and have flowers in a variety of colours and a shape which often resembles that of the rose. A fair number of species are found in Greece and some of them are endemic. *R. asiaticus*, a plant from the eastern Mediterranean, is one of the most beautiful of the ranunculi. It is a perennial with an erect, hairy stem; the leaves at the base are ovate and toothed, in contrast to the upper leaves which are deeply dissected. The flower is usually white or pink, more rarely red or yellow with 5 or more petals and 5 narrow ovate greenish sepals, a characteristic generally differentiating the ranunculi from the anemones with which they are often confused. Found in phrygana, fields, rocky locations, and olive groves.

Peloponnese, Crete, Aegean, Rhodes | 15-30cm ↑ |

1 2 **3 4 5** 6 7 8 9 10 11 12

Ranunculus bullatus L.
Ranunculus bullatus

One of the few ranunculi which flower in the autumn. It has a hairy, erect stem and ovate leaves, delicately toothed and stalked, which are all concentrated in a rosette at the base of the plant. The flowers are yellow with 5-12 petals and many stamens. Found in phrygana, stony locations, and on slopes.

Sterea, S. Greece, Crete, islands | 10-20cm ↑ |

1 2 3 4 5 6 7 **8 9 10** 11 12

Ranunculus ficaria L.

Lesser celandine

A perennial plant with many forms. The stem is smooth and the leaves are deep green, smooth, and heart-shaped with a long stalk. The flowers are solitary, as is the case with nearly all the ranunculi; they are yellow with 8-12 narrow, glossy petals and 3 sepals which are half the length of the petals. Found in damp, shady locations.

Distributed | 5-30cm ↑ | 🏔 ⚓ ☠

| 1 | 2 | 3 | 4 | 5 | 6 | 7 | 8 | 9 | 10 | 11 | 12 |

RESEDACEAE

Reseda alba L.

White mignonette

The white reseda has an erect stem with alternate leaves, deeply divided and with lanceolate, wavy lobes. The small, white flowers are arranged in a dense ear-like inflorescence and have 5 fringed petals and 5 smaller sepals. Found in barren, stony locations, on sandy beaches and in fields. The name of the genus comes from the Latin *resido*, meaning relax and refers to the supposed soothing properties of the plant.

Attica, Peloponnese, Aegean, Crete | 30-80cm ↑ | 🏔 ⚓

| 1 | 2 | 3 | 4 | 5 | 6 | 7 | 8 | 9 | 10 | 11 | 12 |

Reseda lutea L.
Wild mignonette

The yellow reseda is a slightly smaller plant with undulating leaves, very dissected and with narrow lobes. Its flowers are arranged in a spike similar to that of *R. alba*, but the florets are ochre-yellow with 6 petals and the same number of sepals. Found in barren places, fields, and on roadsides.

Distributed | 20-60cm ↑ | ▲ ⚓

1 2 3 4 5 6 7 8 9 10 11 12

Reseda luteola L.
Weld, Dyer's rocket

This has lanceolate, entire leaves, and flowers with 4 sepals and the same number of fringed petals. The leaves of the plant contain very strong pigments, which were known to Dioscurides. The colours they produce range from yellow to an oil shade, and there are Coptic fabrics more than 1,500 years old which were dyed with them and still retain their colour. Found in barren places, on roadsides, on slopes, and in ruins.

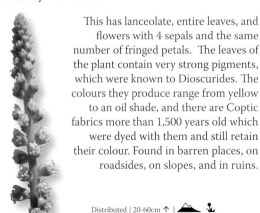

Distributed | 20-60cm ↑ | ▲ ⚓

1 2 3 4 5 6 7 8 9 10 11 12

Geum coccineum SIBTH. & SMITH

ROSACEAE

Geum coccineum

A perennial with an erect stem and hairy leaves, those at the base deeply divided and up to 14cm, the upper leaves smaller. The flowers are red or orange-red with 5 heart-shaped petals and a diameter of up to 4cm; the stamens are numerous. Found in meadows and in shady locations in the mountains of northern Greece.

Thrace, Macedonia, Epirus, Thessaly | Up to 70cm ↑ |

1 2 3 4 5 6 7 8 9 10 11 12

Prunus prostrata LEBILL.

ROSACEAE

Prostrate cherry

A small, deciduous creeping shrub which likes to hug rocks and stones, presenting a unique picture during the flowering period. It has crooked, woody stems and small leaves that are ovate or elliptic and saw-edged. The flowers are whitish-pink in colour and the fruits are small, red berries. Found on rocks in the mountain and alpine zone.

Macedonia, Epirus, Sterea, Peloponnese, Crete | Up to 2m → |

1 2 3 4 5 6 7 8 9 10 11 12

Rosa

In one of the many myths relating to the rose, it is mentioned that the flower was created at the time of the birth of Aphrodite, who rose out of the waves. According to another myth, bare-footed Aphrodite was trying to save Adonis from the madness of Ares when she trod on a thorn of the plant and a drop of her blood gave the flower its rose-colour. Homer makes Aphrodite anoint the dead body of Hector with rose oil in the Iliad. The most beautiful of all flowers - the flower of love and the 'mystical rose' of the Virgin Mary - includes around 200 species throughout the world. Fifteen of them grow in Greece, all with the common name of wild rose.

R. pendulina (the alpine rose) has purple flowers and is found in the mountains of northern Greece.

Rosa canina L. / syn. *Rosa corymbifera*　　　ROSACEAE
Dog rose

A bush with very thorny branches and a height of up to 3 metres. The thorns are curved with a flat base. The flowers are pink, rarely white, solitary or more usually in corymbs of 3-10 with a diameter of up to 6cm. The leaves have 5-7 leaflets, 3-5cm, and are ovate, smooth, and lanceolate at the tips, saw-edged with relatively large teeth. The fruit is ovoid, and red. This is probably the dog rose mentioned by Theophrastus. Found in thickets and in rocky places.

Distributed | Up to 3m ↑ |

| 1 | 2 | 3 | 4 | 5 | 6 | 7 | 8 | 9 | 10 | 11 | 12 |

Rosa pulverulenta M. Bieb. / syn. *Rosa glutinosa*　　　ROSACEAE
Rosa pulverulenta

A small bush with strong stems and thorns that are light in colour, linear or slightly curved. The leaves have 5-7 leaflets and are almost round, toothed and with many glands which give them a dusty texture. The flowers are solitary, and are white or light pink in colour on short flower-stalks. Found in the mountain zone throughout almost the whole of Greece.

Distributed | 1-1,50m ↑ |

| 1 | 2 | 3 | 4 | 5 | 6 | 7 | 8 | 9 | 10 | 11 | 12 |

Rosa sempervirens L.

ROSACEAE

Rosa sempervirens

A perennial shrub, the only evergreen of all the wild roses, with many long, climbing branches which reach to a great height. The leaves have 3-7 leaflets which are lanceolate, saw-edged, and smooth with a leathery texture. The flowers are white and arranged in corymbs of 3-10, with 5 petals and a diameter of up to 6cm. Blooming is so profuse that the flower-bearing stems almost disappear beneath the multitude of flowers. Found in forested areas and thickets.

Distributed | 2-8m ↑ |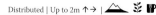

| 1 | 2 | 3 | 4 | 5 | 6 | 7 | 8 | 9 | 10 | 11 | 12 |

Rubus sanctus SCHREB. / syn. *Rubus ulmifolius*

ROSACEAE

Bramble, blackberry

This is the burning bush of the Bible, hence its name. It is a perennial, climbing and branching bush with long, slender stems that are very thorny. The leaves are composite with 3-5 ovate, toothed leaflets, lighter coloured on the underside. The flowers are about 2cm in diameter with long thorny stalks, arranged in loose spikes. There are 5 petals, white or pink, and numerous stamens. The fruits – blackberries – are edible. Normally found on the edges of fields, in hedgerows, and abandoned fields.

Distributed | Up to 2m ↑ → |

| 1 | 2 | 3 | 4 | 5 | 6 | 7 | 8 | 9 | 10 | 11 | 12 |

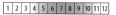

Sarcopoterium spinosum (L.) Spach

ROSACEAE

Thorny burnet

A perennial, dense, head-shaped phrygano plant, very thorny, and similar in form to *E. akantothmnos*. The leaves are small and consist of many leaflets. The beautiful, small, red fleshy fruits are very characteristic. Found in phrygana and in thickets.

Distributed | 30-60cm ↑ → | ▲ ▬

| 1 | 2 | 3 | 4 | 5 | 6 | 7 | 8 | 9 | 10 | 11 | 12 |

RUBIACEAE

Asperula incana Sm. / syn. *Asperula pubescens*

RUBIACEAE

Asperula incana

| 1 | 2 | 3 | 4 | 5 | 6 | 7 | 8 | 9 | 10 | 11 | 12 |

The asperulae are small, herbaceous plants or phrygana which have typical small flowers with a long tube, usually pink or white, and stems that are square in cross-section. More than 30 species are found in Greece, and many of them are endemic. *A. incana* is a perennial, small and hairy phrygano plant with linear leaves, sharply pointed at the tip, which grow in whorls of 6. The flowers are pink with a long tube, in dense heads. Found in rocky locations, phrygana, and on slopes.

A. taygetea, with ▶ a distribution in southern Greece, is a similar plant with whitish flowers.

Crete | 20-40cm ↑ | ▲ ▬

Putoria calabrica (L.F.) DC.
RUBIACEAE

Putoria

A small, normally spreading, phrygana plant with a rank odour. It has a woody stem and opposite leaves which are lanceolate, fleshy and smooth. The flowers resemble those of asperula, and have 4 triangular lobes, a long tube, and develop in corymbs. Found in rocky places from the coastal to the alpine zone.

Distributed | 10-25cm → | 1 2 3 4 5 6 **7 8 9** 10 11 12

RUTACEAE

Ruta chalepensis L.
RUTACEAE

Fringed rue

A perennial, herbaceous plant or small shrub with erect stems, becoming woody at the base, and deeply-cut leaves with ovate, elongated lobes. The yellow flowers have 4-5 ovate, very characteristic fringed petals and flat lanceolate, stippled sepals. The plant, which emits a heavy scent, has been used from the past to this day as a menstrual stimulant. Found in rocky places, amidst ruins, and in gorges.

Peloponnese, Aegean, Crete | 20-80cm → | 1 2 **3 4 5 6** 7 8 9 10 11 12

Saxifraga chrysosplenifolia Boiss.

Saxifraga chrysosplenifolia

A perennial, herbaceous plant with kidney-shaped leaves, toothed, rather fleshy and stalked; the leaves on the stem are stalkless. The flowers have ovate petals which are white with red spots. The name of the genus comes from the Latin, meaning 'that which breaks the rocks', probably referring to the picture presented by the plant which usually grows amongst clefts in rocks. The plant is endemic to the southern Balkans.

Distributed | 10-50cm → | 1 2 3 4 5 6 7 8 9 10 11 12

Bellardia trixago (L.) All.

Bellardia

This is an elegant, perennial herbaceous plant with a strong, erect stem and opposite leaves which are downy, elongated, toothed, usually fleshy, and often have a russet-coloured lip. The whitish-pink flowers are arranged in typical pyramid-shaped spikes. Every flower has a large, undivided lower lip, the upper lip smaller and trilobate, and grows from the four-lobed downy calyx. Found in phrygana and fields.

Distributed | 10-50cm ↑ | 1 2 3 4 5 6 7 8 9 10 11 12

Digitalis grandiflora MILLER
Foxglove

SCROPHULARIACEAE

This imposing plant with its large flowers shaped like church bells can reach a height of up to 1 metre. It is an herbaceous perennial with a robust, hairy, erect stem and elongated, lanceolate and lightly toothed leaves which are hairy on the underside. The yellowish flowers, which develop in a loose raceme, usually have a larger lower lip and dark veining on the inside; they often reach a length of 5cm. Found in woods, clearings, and meadows in the alpine zone.

Macedonia, Epirus, Thessaly | 0,50-1m ↑ | ▲ ↓ ♖ ☠ | 1 2 3 4 5 6 7 8 9 10 11 12

Digitalis lanata EHRH.
Digitalis lanata

SCROPHULARIACEAE

A perennial plant with an erect, hairy stem and leaves that are elongated, lanceolate, and eyelash-like at the base. The flowers are ochre-coloured with reddish-brown veining, almost spherical with a large, curving, whitish lip, and develop in dense spikes. The calyces are very hairy. Like the other species of *digitalis*, it is considered to be a strong cardiac stimulant. Found in forests and thickets.

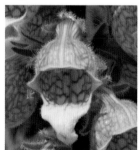

Thrace, Macedonia, Epirus | 0,4-1m ↑ | ▲ ↓ ♖ ☠ | 1 2 3 4 5 6 7 8 9 10 11 12

Linaria peloponnesiaca Boiss. & Heldr.
Toadflax

One of the most beautiful of the Linariae, this is distinguished by its dense, ochre-yellow, grape cluster-like inflorescence. It is a perennial, smooth and with an erect stem and linear, alternate leaves. The flowers have a typical long, curved spur and a hairy calyx. Found in stony places and clearings in the moun-tain and alpine zone.

Thrace, Macedonia, Epirus, Thessaly, Sterea, Peloponnese | 20-40cm ↑ |

| 1 | 2 | 3 | 4 | 5 | 6 | 7 | 8 | 9 | 10 | 11 | 12 |

Parentucellia latifolia (L.) Caruel
Southern red bartsia

SCROPHULARIACEAE

| 1 | 2 | 3 | 4 | 5 | 6 | 7 | 8 | 9 | 10 | 11 | 12 |

This small, hairy, herbaceous annual has an erect stem, often russet-col-oured, and small, deeply toothed and opposite leaves. The tiny, reddish-pink flowers have a trilobate lower lip, a tubular toothed calyx, and develop in the form of a dense ear. It is a semi-parasitic plant which absorbs nutrients from the rhizomes of plants in its neighbourhood. Found in stony locations, phrygana, and on the perimeters of fields.

Distributed | 5-25cm ↑ |

Parentucellia viscosa (L.) Caruel
Yellow bartsia

A glandy, hairy herbaceous plant with an erect stem. The leaves and bracts are opposite, lanceolate, and saw-edged. The flowers are arranged in a terminal, elongated spike, yellow, with a large, trilobate lower lip and a tubular calyx with long lobes. Found in damp places, on the banks of streams, and in fields.

Distributed | 10-50cm ↑ |

| 1 | 2 | 3 | 4 | 5 | 6 | 7 | 8 | 9 | 10 | 11 | 12 |

Scrophularia heterophylla Willd.
Scrophularia heterophylla

The scrophulariae are herbaceous plants, usually strong-smelling, with small, almost round and bag-like flowers which are partly covered by little sepals. *S. heterophylla* has deeply-toothed leaves, toothed or deeply torn and rather fleshy. The flowers are dark red with a white lip in a loose, pyramid-shaped and leafless spike. Found amidst old walls and on rocky slopes, often near the sea.

Distributed | 30-80cm ↑ |

| 1 | 2 | 3 | 4 | 5 | 6 | 7 | 8 | 9 | 10 | 11 | 12 |

Scrophularia lucida L.

Scrophularia lucida

A perennial, hairless plant with a strong stem, russet-coloured and branching, and opposite leaves, deeply divided with narrow, toothed lobes. The flowers are greenish-red and arranged in elongated, leafless, pyramid-shaped spikes. The two butterfly-shaped petals and semi-circular sepals which have white, membranous lips are characteristic. Found in fields, on roadsides, and on slopes.

Thessaly, Sterea, Aegean, Rhodes, Crete | 30-80cm ↑ | 🏔 ⚓ ☠

| 1 | 2 | 3 | 4 | 5 | 6 | 7 | 8 | 9 | 10 | 11 | 12 |

Scrophularia peregrina L.

Nettle-leaved figwort

An annual with an erect, hollow stem and heart-shaped, toothed leaves. The flowers are blackish-red on long stalks which grow in the leaf axils. The sepals, in contrast to those of S. heterophylla and S. lucida, are pointed at the tip. The flowers are rather spreading. Found in olive groves, gorges, and gullies.

Distributed | 30-80cm ↑ | 🏔 ⚓ ☠

| 1 | 2 | 3 | 4 | 5 | 6 | 7 | 8 | 9 | 10 | 11 | 12 |

Verbascum arcturus L.

Verbascum arcturus

The mulleins, as the various species of *Verbascum* are generally known, are downy, herbaceous or phrygano plants with flowers consisting of five parts and usually yellow. More than 40 species grow in Greece; some of these are endemic, such as *V. arcturus* which is only found on Crete. It has an erect stem and toothed, very hairy leaves concentrated at the base. The flowers are yellow with a long stalk, in loose, elongated and pyramid-shaped spikes. Found on vertical cliffs and slopes, and often in ravines.

Crete | Up to 70cm ↑ | ⛰ ⚘

| 1 | 2 | 3 | 4 | 5 | 6 | 7 | 8 | 9 | 10 | 11 | 12 |

Verbascum macrurum Ten.

Verbascum macrurum

| 1 | 2 | 3 | 4 | 5 | 6 | 7 | 8 | 9 | 10 | 11 | 12 |

A biennial, downy plant which reaches an impressive height. It has large, stalkless, rather wavy lanceolate leaves with strong veining. The flowers are stalkless and arranged in a very dense, intensely hairy, ear-like inflorescence. Found in stony places, barren fields and on roadsides.

Crete, Peloponnese, Ionian Islands | Up to 1.20m ↑ | ⛰ ⚘

Verbascum sinuatum L.

Verbascum sinuatum

This is the most frequently occurring species of *Verbascum*; the leaves at the base are large and deeply divided with a very undulating lip. A number of smaller stems grow out from the central stem and all bear many little axillary groups of a few flowers along their length. Found in fields, sandy locations, and on roadsides.

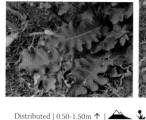

Distributed | 0.50-1.50m ↑ |

| 1 | 2 | 3 | 4 | 5 | 6 | 7 | 8 | 9 | 10 | 11 | 12 |

Verbascum spinosum L.

Spiny mullein

A beautiful perennial phrygano plant which forms hemispherical clumps. The stems are branching, very spiny and have small, lanceolate, downy leaves. The flowers are yellow, solitary, and with a diameter of up to 2cm. Found in stony locations in the White Mountains.

Crete | Up to 0.50m ↑ → |

| 1 | 2 | 3 | 4 | 5 | 6 | 7 | 8 | 9 | 10 | 11 | 12 |

Verbascum undulatum LAM.
SCROPHULARIACEAE

Verbascum undulatum

A biennial, downy plant with strong, erect stems and large wavy leaves in a rosette which develops during the first year. The large yellow flowers have a diameter of up to 5cm and grow in small groups in an elongated, loose spike. Found in abandoned fields, on roadsides, and in barren places.

Epirus | 50-150cm ↑ | 🔺 ⚑

| 1 | 2 | 3 | 4 | 5 | 6 | 7 | 8 | 9 | 10 | 11 | 12 |

Veronica glauca SM.
SCROPHULARIACEAE

Blue speedwell

The veronicae are small, herbaceous plants whose flowers typically have 4 unevenly-sized petals; the upper one is larger, and the lower one smaller than the two in the middle. *V. glauca* has branching stems and grey, ovate and toothed leaves. The little light blue flowers have a white fleck in the centre, a long flower-stalk and grow in terminal racemes. Found in stony places in the mountain zone.

Distributed | Up to 15cm ↑ | 🔺 ⚓

| 1 | 2 | 3 | 4 | 5 | 6 | 7 | 8 | 9 | 10 | 11 | 12 |

Atropa belladonna L.
SOLANACEAE

Deadly nightshade

Care should be taken with this plant - the 'beautiful lady' (belladonna) - because it is extremely poisonous. A perennial, it exceeds 1 metre in height and has large, lanceolate and stalked leaves. The brown, bell-shaped flowers have a five-lobed calyx which is pointed at the tip, on a short, hairy stalk, and usually grow singly in the leaf axils. The fruit is a small, cherry-like berry. Found in the forests of northern Greece.

Thrace, Macedonia, Epirus, Thessaly | 0.50 - 1.30m ↑ | ☉ ☠ ⚰ | 1 2 3 4 5 6 7 8 9 10 11 12

Datura stramonium L.
SOLANACEAE

Thorn apple

This is a rank-smelling, poisonous and hallucinogenic plant, due to the active constituents it contains - hyoscyamine, scopolamine and atropine. The plant is of American origin; it is an annual and has large, usually palmately lobed leaves. The flowers are white, trumpet-like and can reach a length of 10cm. The calyx is also large and has triangular lobes; it covers more than half of the tube. The fruit is a large, spiny capsule. Found on waste ground, amidst rubble, on roadsides and in ditches.

Distributed | 0.40-1.20m ↑ | ☉ ☠ ⚰ | 1 2 3 4 5 6 7 8 9 10 11 12

Hyoscyamus albus L.   SOLANACEAE
White henbane

This is also a poisonous plant which is avoided by all animals except for the pig – hence the name *Hyoscyamus* which means 'pig-bean' and derives from the Greek words *hys* (pig) and *kyamos* (bean). The large, hairy, soft leaves are toothed; more rarely they are almost entire. It has yellowish tubular flowers with unequal lips and a large, hairy calyx with triangular lobes. Found in wasteland, amidst rubble, and on roadsides.

Distributed | 30-90cm ↑→ | 🏔 ⚓ ☠ ▮ | 1 2 3 4 5 6 7 8 9 10 11 12

Mandragora autumnalis BERTOL. / syn. *Mandragora officinarum*   SOLANACEAE
Mandrake

The anthropomorphic root of the mandrake, combined with its medicinal properties which have been known since antiquity, is the reason why there are so many beliefs about the plant. The very large leaves grow almost immediately from the roots and form an impressive prostrate rosette, in the centre of which the blue-violet bell-shaped flowers develop. Found in stony locations and barren fields.

Distributed | Up to 20/50cm ↑→ | 🏔 ⚓ ▮ ☠ | 1 2 3 4 5 6 7 8 9 10 11 12

Nicotiana glauca GRAHAM

SOLANACEAE

Tree tobacco

This is a naturalised tree or bush which originated from South America. The flowers are tubular and yellow, with a diameter of about 5 mm and a length of 3-4cm, and arranged in loose spikes. The leaves are lanceolate and grey - hence the name. It is cultivated as a decorative plant and is self-sowing on old walls, cliffs, roadsides and in abandoned fields. It flowers nearly the whole year round and is a close relation of *Nicotiana tabacum*, cultivated for its leaves which produce our well-known tobacco for cigarettes and cigars. Many parts of the plant are poisonous.

Distributed | 2-5m ↑ | 1 2 3 4 5 6 7 8 9 10 11 12

STYRACACEAE

Styrax officinalis L.

STYRACACEAE

Storax

A small tree or bush with ovate, slightly downy leaves. The white, bell-like and nodding flowers are very fragrant and grow in bunches. At maturity, they produce round fruits and seeds. When the bark of the plant is scratched, it produces a resinous, pleasant-smelling substance which has been used in perfumery since antiquity. According to the myth, the plant originated from Crete and was introduced to mainland Greece by Radamanthys, the brother of Minos; both were sons of Zeus and Europa. Found in cool locations, on the banks of rivers and in the zone of Mediterranean maquis.

Distributed | Up to 5m ↑ | 1 2 3 4 5 6 7 8 9 10 11 12

Daphne oleoides Schreb.

THYMELEACEAE

Daphne oleoides

The scientific name of these shrubs - *Daphne* - causes confusion in Greece since, from ancient times, the name *daphni* has been given to that other plant unfortunately baptized *Laurus nobilis* (bay) by *Linnaeus*. *D. oleoides* is a shrub with fleshy, ovate leaves and beautiful white, fragrant flowers with 4 long, pointed-tipped lobes which grow in groups of 3-6 in terminal, head-like bunches. Found in alpine, mountainous and rocky locations, in thickets and in open forests.

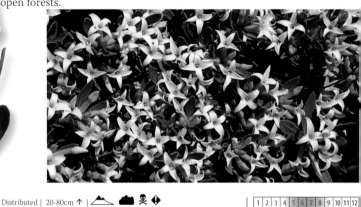

Distributed | 20-80cm ↑ |

1 2 3 4 5 6 7 8 9 10 11 12

Daphne sericea Vahl.

THYMELEACEAE

Daphne sericea

This beautiful, much-branched shrub has leaves that are hairy on the underside, lanceolate, and rather fleshy. The fragrant flowers, which have a silky texture, are hairy on the outside and grow in bunches. They are usually pink, but on maturity acquire shades of cream. Found in stony locations, usually in the mountain zone.

Sterea, Crete | Up to 60cm ↑ |

1 2 3 4 5 6 7 8 9 10 11 12

Thymelaea hirsuta (L.) ENDL.

Thymelaea hirsuta

A much-branched shrub with densely downy stems.The leaves are numerous, small, fleshy and overlapping. The yellow flowers grow in bunches and appear in autumn; flowering often continues until the spring. Found in stony locations, near the sea.

Distributed | 40-100cm ↑ | 1 2 3 4 5 6 7 8 9 10 11 12

Thymelaea tartonraira (L.) ALL.

Thymelaea tartonraira

A small, much-branched phrygano plant or shrub with lanceolate, silver-coloured and hairy leaves. The flowers are axillary, yellow with 4 sharply-pointed lobes and downy on the outside, often many together. Found in stony locations, phrygana, and on slopes.

Distributed | 20-50cm ↑ | 1 2 3 4 5 6 7 8 9 10 11 12

● *Zelkova abelicea* (Lam.) Boiss. / syn. *Zelkova cretica*   ULMACEAE
Zelkova abelicea

Endemic to the mountains of Crete, Zelkova is the only representative of this Asiatic genus in Europe. It was from the branches of this rare tree that shepherds used to make their crooks, and since it bore no resemblance to any other tree in the Cretan mountains they called it *anégnoro*, meaning unrecognisable. The very tiny population of this unique tree, which has been characterized as threatened, is in need of protection.

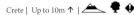

Crete | Up to 10m ↑ | 🔺 🌳 ◆   1 2 3 4 5 6 7 8 9 10 11 12

UMBELLIFERAE

These are herbaceous plants, distinguished by their inflorescence which takes the form of an umbel. The little flowers of the various genera, which normally have 5 petals, often resemble each other and this makes their differentiation difficult. The family includes a multitude of species, from the most common such as fennel (*Foeniculum vulgare*) to the extremely rare (e.g. *Bupleurum kakiscalae*). The latter, which has leaves in a large and beautiful rosette and yellow flowers, is one of the rarest plants in the world, since there are only a few individual examples to be found in a biotope of a few square metres in the White Mountains.

Conium maculatum L.   UMBELLIFERAE
Hemlock

This is the most famous of the umbelliferae, since it was the poison of this plant that killed Socrates, the greatest of the philosophers. The plant received its name in antiquity due to the funnel-like leaves which are deeply divided with toothed lobes. It has a much-branching habit with ridged, hollow stems.The umbel with the little white flowers has up to 20 rays that are uneven in length. Found on the edges of fields, in hedgerows, and amidst rubble.

Distributed | Up to 1m ↑ | 🔺 🌱 ⚔ 🍶   1 2 3 4 5 6 7 8 9 10 11 12

Crithmum maritimum L.

Rock samphire

This is an annual plant with branching stems. The fleshy leaves are elongated and of a characteristic grey colour. The flowers are white in a dense umbel. The leaves, which are edible, are collected before flowering and preserved in salt. Found on cliffs, walls and sands, always near the sea.

Distributed | 20-40cm ↑ | △ ⚓ ⚑ | 1 2 3 4 5 6 7 8 9 10 11 12

Daucus carota L.

UMBELLIFERAE

Wild carrot

This is a polymorphic plant with a branching stem and deeply-divided leaves. The umbels are large with a multitude of rays and the flowers white or purple, always with dark purple at the centre. After flowering, the umbel closes to form a ball. The plant, which has a tuberous rhizome, is the progenitor of the cultivated carrot. Found in fields and on roadsides.

Distributed | 30-80cm ↑ | △ ⚓ ⚑ | 1 2 3 4 5 6 7 8 9 10 11 12

Eryngium creticum Lam.

Small-headed blue eryngo

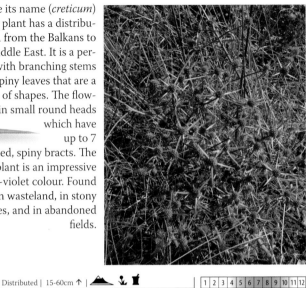

Despite its name (*creticum*) this plant has a distribution from the Balkans to the Middle East. It is a perennial with branching stems and spiny leaves that are a variety of shapes. The flowers are in small round heads which have up to 7 elongated, spiny bracts. The whole plant is an impressive bluish-violet colour. Found on wasteland, in stony places, and in abandoned fields.

Distributed | 15-60cm ↑ | ⛰ ⚓ ☗ | 1 | 2 | 3 | 4 | 5 | 6 | 7 | 8 | 9 | 10 | 11 | 12 |

Eryngium maritimum L.

Sea holly

This plant has characteristic large, spiny and palmately lobed periblastic leaves and branching stems which are grey or violet in colour. The little, bluish-white flowers occur in round heads which have wide, spiny bracts. Found on sandy beaches.

Distributed | 15-60cm ↑ | ⛰ ⚓ ☗ | 1 | 2 | 3 | 4 | 5 | 6 | 7 | 8 | 9 | 10 | 11 | 12 |

Ferula communis L.
Giant fennel

This is a perennial plant with a large, thick, light stem and deeply-cut leaves which resemble those of fennel. The yellow flowers are arranged in terminal, round umbels which have up to 40 rays. In the past, the dried stems of the plant were used to make impromptu furniture. The fleshy content of the stems burns slowly, and for this reason it was used to make torches in antiquity. It is with such a torch that, according to mythology, *Prometheus* brought fire to the human race. Found on roadsides, cliffs, and in fields.

Distributed | Up to 3m ↑ | 🔺 ⚘ | 1 | 2 | 3 | 4 | 5 | 6 | 7 | 8 | 9 | 10 | 11 | 12 |

Ferulago nodosa (L.) Boiss.
Ferulago

A plant resembling *Ferula*, but differentiated from it by the presence of round swellings at the places where the stems branch, which give it its name (nodosa). The leaves are deeply cut with straight lobes and are all concentrated at the base of the plant. The yellow flowers are arranged in an umbel which has up to 15 rays. Found in stony places and barren fields.

Distributed | Up to 2m ↑ | 🔺 ⚘ | 1 | 2 | 3 | 4 | 5 | 6 | 7 | 8 | 9 | 10 | 11 | 12 |

Orlaya grandiflora (L.) Hoffm.

UMBELLIFERAE

Orlaya

The plant takes its name from the extremely large petals of the peripheral flowers of the umbel, which consists of up to 12 rays of white flowers; this characteristic makes it easily identifiable. The leaves are deeply divided with ovate lobes. Found in olive groves, fields, and on roadsides.

Distributed | 20-40cm ↑ |

| 1 | 2 | 3 | 4 | 5 | 6 | 7 | 8 | 9 | 10 | 11 | 12 |

Smyrnium olusatrum L.

UMBELLIFERAE

Alexanders

A biennial, aromatic plant with a ridged, hollow stem and large leaves that are trilobate or consist of three leaflets which have thin teeth on the lips. The flowers are yellow, in umbels with up to 18 rays. Found in abandoned fields, olive groves, and ditches.

Distributed | Up to 1m ↑ |

| 1 | 2 | 3 | 4 | 5 | 6 | 7 | 8 | 9 | 10 | 11 | 12 |

Smyrnium rotundifolium D.C.

Smyrnium rotundifolium

This is also a biennial, with a ridged but not hollow stem; the upper leaves are round and periblastic, making the plant easy to recognize. The flowers are yellow, in umbels which have up to 12 rays. Found in olive groves, thickets, and in dry locations.

Distributed | 30-60cm ↑ |

| 1 | 2 | 3 | 4 | 5 | 6 | 7 | 8 | 9 | 10 | 11 | 12 |

Tordylium apulum L.

Tordylium

A plant with a ridged stem and downy leaves, the lower ones heart-shaped, toothed or trilobate, the upper ones ribbon-like. The flowers are small and white; only one petal of each peripheral flower is larger. The very aromatic leaves give a special flavour to salads. Found in stony locations, olive groves, and fields.

Distributed | 10-50cm ↑ |

| 1 | 2 | 3 | 4 | 5 | 6 | 7 | 8 | 9 | 10 | 11 | 12 |

Centranthus ruber (L.) DC.
Red valerian

VALERIANACEAE

This very beautiful, grey-green plant which can often be seen in gardens and in pots has erect stems with wide, opposite, entire leaves that are sharply pointed and can reach a length of 12cm. The lower leaves have a little stalk while the upper ones are stalkless. The small, tubular, pink flowers have a five-lobed corolla and a long, slender spur, and grow in a dense cluster. Found in rocky places and on slopes.

Distributed | 30-80cm ↑ |

| 1 | 2 | 3 | 4 | 5 | 6 | 7 | 8 | 9 | 10 | 11 | 12 |

Centranthus sieberii HELDR.

Centranthus sieberii

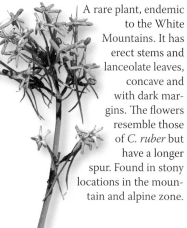

A rare plant, endemic to the White Mountains. It has erect stems and lanceolate leaves, concave and with dark margins. The flowers resemble those of *C. ruber* but have a longer spur. Found in stony locations in the mountain and alpine zone.

Crete | Up to 30cm ↑ | ▲ ⬇ ◈

| 1 | 2 | 3 | 4 | 5 | 6 | 7 | 8 | 9 | 10 | 11 | 12 |

Valeriana asarifolia DUFR.

Cretan valerian

This is an endemic valerian with a strong, erect stem and distinguished its lower leaves which are long-stalked, kidney-shaped, and slightly toothed, while the upper leaves are deeply divided. The white or pink flowers grow in a dense, head-shaped cluster. Found in rocky places and in phrygana.

Crete, Karpathos | 20-50cm ↑ | ▲ ⬇

| 1 | 2 | 3 | 4 | 5 | 6 | 7 | 8 | 9 | 10 | 11 | 12 |

Valeriana tuberosa L.

Valeriana tubosa

A perennial with a strong, erect and russet-coloured stem. The lower leaves are unlobed and the upper ones deeply divided with extended lobes, that at the tip being longer than the others. The flowers are whitish-pink and grow in dense, round clusters. Found in rocky locations and in barren fields.

V. officinalis, which has medicinal properties, is similar but all of its leaves are deeply divided.

Epirus | Up to 50cm ↑ |

1	2	3	4	5	6	7	8	9	10	11	12

VERBENACEAE

Vitex agnus castus L.

Chaste tree

An aromatic bush with strong, pliable branches. This characteristic gave the name to the genus; the branches had many uses in the past, the most common of which was basket-making (Latin *vitor* = basket-maker). The leaves are composite with lanceolate, elongated, unlobed leaflets. The bluish-white flowers develop in whorls which form a beautiful, long ear-like spike. The two words in the name of this genus, *agnós* (Greek) and *castus* (Latin) mean the same (chaste) and it is no coincidence that this plant is considered to be anaphrodisiac and sedative. Found in ravines and gorges.

Distributed | 1-3m ↑ |

1	2	3	4	5	6	7	8	9	10	11	12

VIOLACEAE

Viola fragrans Sieber

VIOLACEAE

Viola fragrans

The beautiful violets or wild pansies are distinguished by their flowers with five petals - two pairs of similar petals while the fifth protrudes behind, forming a spur. *V. fragrans* has lanceolate leaves and yellow, white or violet flowers. Found in stony locations in the subalpine and alpine zone of the mountains of Crete.

Crete | Up to 30cm ↑ | ▲ ↓ ◆

1	2	3	4	5	6	7	8	9	10	11	12

Viola odorata L.

VIOLACEAE

Sweet violet

This fragrant little violet has basal leaves which are prostrate, heart-shaped, kidney-shaped and long-stalked. The flowers are a deep violet in colour and the sepals ovate. Found in cool locations, and widely cultivated as a decorative plant.

Epirus | 10-30cm ↑ | ▲ ↓ ❀ ❦

1	2	3	4	5	6	7	8	9	10	11	12

Viola rhodopeia BECKER

VIOLACEAE

Viola rhodopeia

A perennial plant, slender and endemic to the Rhodopi mountain chain. The leaves and leaflets are straight-lanceolate with shallow toothing, the leaflets with small lobes at the base. The flowers are yellow or whitish-yellow with pointed sepals. Found in clearings and meadows.

Rhodopi | 10-20cm ↑ | 1 2 3 **4 5 6 7** 8 9 10 11 12

Viola riviniana REICHENB.

VIOLACEAE

Viola riviniana

A widely distributed species, *V. riviniana* is distinguished by its long-stalked, toothed and heart-shaped leaves. The flowers are violet with a central petal that has a white base with dark lines. The spur is relatively long, and the sepals have elongated, pointed lobes. Found in stony locations and forest clearings.

Epirus | Up to 30cm ↑ | 1 2 3 **4 5 6** 7 8 9 10 11 12

MONOCOTYLEDONS

The monocotyledons (Monocotyledonae) constitute the second large class of angiosperms. As their name indicates, the seeds have one seed-leaf. The leaves of the monocotyledons are characterized by parallel veining, in contrast to those of the dicotyledons which have a network of veining.

AGAVACEAE 188

AMARYLLIDACEAE 188

ARACEAE 191

DIOSCOREACEAE 196

GRAMINEAE 196

IRIDACEAE 197

LILIACEAE 208

ORCHIDACEAE 229

Agave americana L.

Century plant

| 1 | 2 | 3 | 4 | 5 | 6 | 7 | 8 | 9 | 10 | 11 | 12 |

A plant which originates from Mexico but has become acclimatized to Greece and the whole of the Mediterranean area. The leaves are arranged in a rosette, grey, large, fleshy and channelled, up to 2 metres long; they are very spiny on the lips and tip. The agave flowers only once, when it has reached an age of at least 10 ten years; thereafter it dies. However, by that time the plant will already have reproduced, since a multitude of stems have developed from its rhizome. The spike is large on an impressive stalk up to 6 metres in height, with many flower-bearing stems and yellow flowers. Found in hedges and on the sides of roads.

Distributed | More than 8m ↑ |

AMARYLLIDACEAE

Leucojum aestivum L.

Summer snowflake

A perennial, herbaceous plant which grows from a bulb. It has a strong stem which is smooth and angular. The leaves are large and ribbon-like, up to 40cm in length. The flowers are white, in a nodding, loose terminal spike. There are 6 tepals with green stippling on the edges and 6 stamens with yellow anthers. A decorative plant, often found in large clumps in damp locations.

Thrace, Macedonia, Epirus | 35-70cm ↑ |

| 1 | 2 | 3 | 4 | 5 | 6 | 7 | 8 | 9 | 10 | 11 | 12 |

Narcissus

Narcissus, son of the river Kifisos and the nymph Leiropi, was so enamoured of himself that one day, while admiring his reflection in the waters of a spring, he fell in and drowned. From that time onwards, this beautiful plant has preferred the banks of streams and rivers; it has a strong, heady aroma which is perhaps more powerful than that of any other wild flower. The narcissi grow from bulbs. Their flowers are very characteristic; in the centre of the perianth, which is divided into 6 parts, there develops a cup-shaped corolla containing the stamens. The narcissi are represented in Greece by 3 species.

Narcissus poeticus L.
AMARYLLIDACEAE
Pheasant's eye narcissus

The most beautiful of all the narcissi, this has a flattened stem and 3-5 flat leaves of equal length, which are themselves the same length as the stem. The flowers are large, up to 6cm, solitary, with a white perianth and an internal shallow corolla which is wide, yellow and wavy with a red border on the lip. Found in damp meadows in the mountain and sub-alpine zone.

Macedonia, Sterea, Peloponnese, Epirus, Evvia | 20-60cm ↑ | 🔺 ↳ 🌱 | 1 2 **3 4 5 6 7** 8 9 10 11 12

Narcissus serotinus L.
AMARYLLIDACEAE
Narcissus serotinus

The autumn narcissus is a delicate plant with white flowers whose diameter does not exceed 3cm. The internal corona is yellow, and very small. The stem is slender, cylindrical and 20-30cm long. The leaves are usually absent or produced after flowering. Found in stony places, olive groves and loose thickets.

Sterea, Peloponnese, Aegean, Crete | 10-30cm ↑ | 🔺 ↳ | 1 2 3 4 5 6 7 8 **9 10 11** 12

Narcissus tazetta L.
Bunch-flowered narcissus

This is perhaps the most fragrant of all the narcissi, known locally in Greece as 'manousáki'; it is avidly collected and sold in bunches on the open market stalls. It has a stout cylindrical stem, and greyish-green leaves with an angular ridge and a length equal to that of the stem. The perianth is white, 3-4cm in diameter, with an internal yellow corona, up to 5 mm in height. There are up to 12 nodding flowers. Found in damp locations.

The subspecies *N. tazetta* ssp. *aureus* is similar, but the perianth is yellow and the internal corona orange in colour.

Distributed | 20-50cm ↑ | 🏔 🪴 🌱   1 2 3 **4 5 6 7 8 9** 10 11 12

Pancratium maritimum L.
Sea daffodil

This is one of the most beautiful of wild flowers and decorates the beaches every summer. It is a perennial, herbaceous plant that grows from a bulb; its leaves are large and ribbon-like, longer than the stem, and have already withered by the time of flowering. The new leaves appear at the beginning of winter. The flowers are large, funnel-shaped, 3-15 in every umbel, fragrant and white. The anthers are yellow, on six long white stamens. The characteristic fruits resemble pieces of charcoal; they are light in weight and float on the sea, which disperses them along the shore. The beauty of this plant inspired Minoan artists, who depicted it in the palace of Knossos.

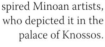

Distributed | 20-60cm ↑ | 🏔 🪴   1 2 3 4 5 6 **7 8 9** 10 11 12

Sternbergia lutea (L.) Ker-Gawl. ex Spreng.   AMARYLLIDACEAE
Common sternbergia

Its flower resembling that of a crocus, *S. lutea* is a perennial herbaceous plant that grows from a bulb. It has lanceolate, elongated, narrow leaves which develop during flowering. The flowers are yellow, with a membrane-like spathe at their base and a perianth divided into 6 lanceolate tepals up to 6cm in length. There are 6 yellow anthers. Found in shady, stony places, olive groves etc. It is often cultivated as a decorative plant.

S. sicula is similar, but smaller with leaves that appear after flowering.

Sterea, Peloponnese, Crete | 10-30cm ↑ | 🔺 ↓ 🌿   1 2 3 4 5 6 7 8 9 10 11 12

ARACEAE

The arums, and the Araceae in general, are easily recognised by the characteristic shape of their flower-head which consists of a tubular or funnel-shaped sheath (spathe) around an elongated spadix which bears tiny flowers, male above and female below. The leaves are usually dart-shaped on a long stalk. Pollination is carried out by insects which are attracted by the rank smell - which can be very pronounced – exuded by at least some of the *Araceae*. The attraction of pollinators by this method has given the name to this family, and to its largest species (*Arum*), which derives from the Greek word 'ároma'.

Arisarum vulgare Targ.-Tozz.   ARACEAE
Friar's cowl

One of the smaller members of the family, this is a perennial herbaceous plant, easily identified by the characteristic cylindrical shape of the yellowish-green spathe with its russet stripes. The spadix is slender, cylindrical, and has a curve at the lip of the spathe. The leaves are heart-shaped with a long stalk. Found in stony, shady locations.

Distributed | 20-40cm ↑ | 🔺 ↓ ☠   1 2 3 4 5 6 7 8 9 10 11 12

Arum alpinum Schott & Kotschy
Arum alpinum

ARACEAE

1	2	3	4	5	6	7	8	9	10	11	12

14 species of arum are found in Greece. *A. alpinum* prefers higher altitudes – hence its name. It has an oblong green spathe and a slender spadix. The leaves are large and dart-shaped, with a long stalk. It has almost no aroma, and is found singly or in small colonies, normally hidden by bushes.

Crete, Macedonia, Epirus, Sterea | Up to 50cm ↑ | ⛰ ⚓ ☠

• *Arum creticum* Boiss. & Heldr.
Cretan arum

ARACEAE

This is perhaps the most beautiful *arum* to be found in Greece. The spathe is a brilliant yellow colour, bending at the tip, and the spadix deep yellow and longer than the spathe. The leaves are large and dart-shaped, often slightly billowy. It usually has a sweet and pleasing aroma, more rarely a slightly rank one. The plant is endemic to Crete and Karpathos, and often occurs in large groups.

Crete | Up to 30cm ↑ | ⛰ ⚓ ☠

1	2	3	4	5	6	7	8	9	10	11	12

Arum dioscoridis Sibth.

ARACEAE

Arum dioscuridis

An impressive-looking *arum*, with a yellow, vividly spotted spathe with purple spots on the inside. The spadix is purple and a little shorter than the spathe. Pollination is carried out by flies attracted by the smell of dung that the plant emits during flowering. The leaves are large and dart-like, on a long stalk.

The illustration is by the Austrian artist Ferdinand Bauer (1760-1826), from the classic work by the English botanist John Sibthorp (1758-1796) entitled 'Flora Grae-ca'. This ten-volume work, probably the most important - and at the same time -rarest botanical study in the world, contains stunning illustrations by Bauer and was published after Sibthorp's death in only 25 copies.

Chios, Rhodes | 30-40cm ↑ | 1 2 3 **4 5** 6 7 8 9 10 11 12

Arum idaeum Coustur. & Gand

ARACEAE

Arum idaeum

This beautiful little *arum* is easily recognised by its whitish-green spathe and blackish-purple spadix which does not protrude from the spathe. The leaves are dart-like, and impressively large. During flowering it produces an almost pleasant scent. It is endemic to Crete, and prefers high altitudes. Found beneath cypress and oak trees, often amidst thickets of *Berberis cretica*.

Crete | Up to 40cm ↑ | 1 2 3 **4 5** 6 7 8 9 10 11 12

Arum italicum Schott

Arum italicum

This is the most common arum, found in large populations and preferring shaded places and olive groves. The triangular, dart-like leaves appear very early. The spathe is large, yellow or yellow-green, often with violet shading on the lips. The spadix is yellow and much shorter than the spathe.

A. concinnatum is similar to *A. italicum* and replaces it on the Aegean islands and Crete.

Epirus | 20-60cm ↑ | ◭ ⚓ ☠

1	2	3	4	5	6	7	8	9	10	11	12

Arum maculatum L.

'Lords and ladies', Cuckoo pint

This takes its name from the spots which are often present on its dart-shaped leaves. The spathe is yellowish-green, often with violet shading, and the spadix blackish-purple and reaching almost to the middle of the spathe. Found in forests and clearings.

Thrace, Macedonia, Thessaly, Attica, Evvia, Peloponnese | 20-50cm ↑ | ◭ ▮ ☠

1	2	3	4	5	6	7	8	9	10	11	12

Biarum davisii Turrill

ARACEAE

Cretan biarum

This rare, strange little plant with its barrel-like shape is endemic to Crete and was identified relatively recently. The spathe is cream-coloured with white spots, closed and ovoid-cylindrical, with a height which rarely exceeds 5cm. The spadix is funnel-like, and slender at the end which protrudes from the spathe. It flowers in the autumn, the leaves being produced at quite a late stage. It has no aroma. In the past, it was used on Crete to induce abortion.

 Crete | 5-10cm ↑ |

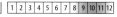 1 2 3 4 5 6 7 8 9 10 11 12

Dracunculus vulgaris Schott

ARACEAE

Dragon arum, Great dragon

An impressive plant, with a height which often exceeds 1 metre. The spathe is lanceolate, purple on the inside and yellowish-green on the outside. The spadix is slender, long and purple, but shorter than the spathe. The leaves are large, deeply cut and wavy with white spots. The stem is very characteristic, bearing a pattern which resembles that of a zebra-skin. During the flowering period, the plant emits a strong, rank odour which attracts flies. This is not a flesh-eating plant, as many people believe. The flies are temporarily trapped to ensure pollination and then they are released. Found on roadsides and in abandoned fields, often in large communities.

Distributed | Up to 1.30m ↑ | 1 2 3 4 5 6 7 8 9 10 11 12

DIOSCOREACEAE

Tamus communis L.
Black bryony

A perennial, climbing, herbaceous plant with a tuberous root and annual stems. The leaves are heart-shaped, smooth and with a long stalk. The flowers are male and female on different plants (unisexual), small and greenish-yellow, the male flowers in a thick raceme, the female flowers more loosely arranged. The seed is a little red berry. Despite the fact that the plant is poisonous, the tender stems are considered an excellent dish after a procedure has been followed in which they are boiled and the water changed. The plant is used as a purgative in folk medicine. Found in thickets and shady locations.

Distributed | Up to 60cm ↑

| 1 | 2 | 3 | 4 | 5 | 6 | 7 | 8 | 9 | 10 | 11 | 12 |

GRAMINEAE

Ammophila arenaria (L.) Link
Marram grass

This little arenaceous plant which has chosen sand as its biotope, is not, of course, interesting because of its flower, which looks like a corn-ear, but for the beautiful clumps in which it develops on the sand dunes. It is a very important plant where the stability of this biotope is concerned, since its network of roots holds the sandy soil together. The name comes from the Greek words 'fílos' and 'ámmos', meaning 'lover of sand', and refers very aptly to its preferred habit.

Attica, Peloponnese, Aegean, Rhodes, Crete | 0.40-1.20m ↑

| 1 | 2 | 3 | 4 | 5 | 6 | 7 | 8 | 9 | 10 | 11 | 12 |

IRIDACEAE

Crocus

From the autumn to the spring, a large group of flowers decorates the Greek landscape. In particular the winter crocus, which very often springs up out of the snow, offers pictures of unparalleled beauty in a season when most plants are dormant and preparing for spring. The crocuses have certain special characteristics, as for example the growth of flower and leaves directly from the bulb and the presence of three stigmas – the part of the plant which is harvested. Safran, as this important substance is called, consists of the stigmas of *C. sativus*, the cultivated crocus, which is grown in Greece around Kozani and yields a product of superb quality. The importance of the crocus even in antiquity is apparent from the famous wall-paintings at Knossos and on Santorini.

The plant, like many others, acquired its name from Greek mythology. While playing with his friend Krokos, Hermes accidentally killed him. Where the young man fell the crocus sprang up, its stigmas being three drops of his blood; he subsequently gave the plant its name.

Crocus boryi GAY

IRIDACEAE

Crocus boryi

A dead-white flower, yellow at the base. The stigmas are yellowish-orange, torn into fine threads, and shorter than the perianth. The anthers are white, shorter than, or the same length as, the stigmas. The leaves are linear and narrow, reaching to the height of the flowers. Found in stony places, on slopes, and in olive groves.

Sterea, Peloponnese, Crete, Aegean | Up to 15cm ↑ |

| 1 | 2 | 3 | 4 | 5 | 6 | 7 | 8 | 9 | 10 | 11 | 12 |

Crocus cartwrightianus Herb.

Greek saffron crocus, Wild saffron crocus

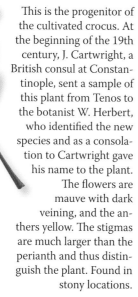

6-part perianth

Anthers

Stigmas

Tube

This is the progenitor of the cultivated crocus. At the beginning of the 19th century, J. Cartwright, a British consul at Constantinople, sent a sample of this plant from Tenos to the botanist W. Herbert, who identified the new species and as a consolation to Cartwright gave his name to the plant. The flowers are mauve with dark veining, and the anthers yellow. The stigmas are much larger than the perianth and thus distinguish the plant. Found in stony locations.

Attica, Peloponnese, Sterea, Crete, Aegean | 5-15cm ↑ | 1 2 3 4 5 6 7 8 9 10 11 12

Crocus chrysantus Herb.

Crocus chrysantus

The name of this plant derives from the Greek words 'chrysós' meaning gold and 'ánthos' meaning flower, and describes the golden yellow colour of the flower. The anthers and the stigmas are the same colour, and much shorter than the perianth. The leaves are narrow, four or more. Found in stony places.

C. olivieri is similar but differs in that the stigmas are divided into two thin threads each, and the plant does not have more than two leaves.

Epirus | 5-12cm ↑ | 1 2 3 4 5 6 7 8 9 10 11 12

Crocus flavus WESTON

Crocus flavus

This is a yellow crocus with a tube that is often brownish-grey. The anthers are also yellow and the stigmas orange and entire. The stamens and stigmas are almost of equal length, shorter than the perianth. There are 6-8 leaves which have not completely developed by the time of flowering. The variety, often cultivated as a decorative plant is found in meadows and clearings.

Epirus | 8-15cm ↑ | ▲▲ ⚘ ❀ | 1 2 3 4 5 6 7 8 9 10 11 12

Crocus laevigatus BORY & CHAUB.

Crocus laevigatus

This is the most widely distributed of the crocuses and has a long tube and parts of the perianth which are white or slightly mauve, each with three violet lines on the outside; more rarely it is completely white. The anthers are white and the stigmas yellow, torn into thin threads a little shorter than, or of equal length with, the perianth. The leaves have a light-coloured ridge at the centre, and develop during the flowering period. Found in stony places, on slopes, and in forests.

Evvia, Attica, Peloponnese, Sterea, Crete, Aegean | 5-15cm ↑ | ▲▲ ⚘ | 1 2 3 4 5 6 7 8 9 10 11 12

Crocus niveus Bowles

Crocus niveus

This crocus, which is endemic to the Peloponnese, bears a resemblance to *C. boryi*, since it has a white perianth and yellow throat; it is distinguished, however, by its yellow anthers. The stigmas are orange-yellow, and slightly divided at the tip. The three external tepals have slight mauve shading. Found in olive groves, on slopes, and in stony locations.

Peloponnese | Up to 25cm ↑ | 🔺 ⚱ ◈ | 1 | 2 | 3 | 4 | 5 | 6 | 7 | 8 | 9 | 10 | 11 | 12 |

Crocus oreocreticus B.L. Burtt

Crocus oreocreticus

This crocus is endemic to the mountains of Crete, hence its name '*oreocreticus*', although it is not found in the White Mountains. It greatly resembles *C. cartwrightianus*, but has much shorter stigmas and is darker. Found in stony locations.

Crete | 5-15cm ↑ | 🔺 ⚱ | 1 | 2 | 3 | 4 | 5 | 6 | 7 | 8 | 9 | 10 | 11 | 12 |

Crocus pulchellus Herb.

Crocus pulchellus

The tube is whitish-yellow and the perianth light blue or mauve with a yellow throat and dark lines. The anthers are white and the stigmas orange, torn into thin threads, shorter than the perianth. The leaves appear after flowering. Found in forest clearings.

Thrace, Macedonia, Epirus | 10-15cm ↑ |

| 1 | 2 | 3 | 4 | 5 | 6 | 7 | 8 | 9 | 10 | 11 | 12 |

Crocus sieberi ssp. *sieberi* Gay

IRIDACEAE

Crocus sieberi ssp. sieberi

| 1 | 2 | 3 | 4 | 5 | 6 | 7 | 8 | 9 | 10 | 11 | 12 |

This crocus is endemic to the White Mountains and many little outcrops are covered in it during springtime. It has a white perianth with mauve areas on the outside of three of its parts, and a yellow throat. The anthers are yellow and the stigmas orange, entire and with a flat tip. There are more than five leaves, which have a light-coloured ridge in the centre and are the same length as the flowers. Found in stony locations and meadows, often amongst bushes.

● *Crocus sieberi* ssp. *atticus* (Gay) Boiss. & Orph.

The perianth of this plant is pinkish-mauve with thin, dark veining on the outside of three of its parts, and a yellow throat. The anthers are yellow and the stigmas orange, entire and with a flat tip. There are 3-5 leaves, which have a light-coloured ridge in the centre and are the same length as the anthers. Found in stony places, mountain meadows, and clearings.

Crete (The White Mountains) | 10-15cm ↑ |

Crocus tournefortii GAY IRIDACEAE
Crocus tournefortii

This is one of the most beautiful of the Greek crocuses. The perianth is of light pinkish-mauve shades and the throat yellow. The anthers are white and the stigmas yellow, divided into many threads, and longer than the flower. The leaves are narrow with a white ridge at the centre. Found in stony places and olive groves.

The famous French botanical expert and doctor, Joseph Pitton de Tournefort (1656-1708) travelled around Crete and many Aegean islands, amongst other places, and was the first to describe a multitude of different plants.

Aegean, Peloponnese, Crete | 5-15cm ↑ | 🔺 🔻

| 1 | 2 | 3 | 4 | 5 | 6 | 7 | 8 | 9 | 10 | 11 | 12 |

Gladiolus italicus MILLER IRIDACEAE
Field gladiolus

This is the hyacinth of antiquity, one of the most beautiful wild flowers in the Greek landscape. The strong stem grows from a corm and reaches up to 80cm in height. It has 3-5 leaves, slightly shorter than the stem, with a width of up to 2cm. The flowers are pink, up to 10 in number, on an ear-like spike. It is a very decorative plant and avidly collected for that reason. Found in cultivated fields, olive groves, and meadows.

Distributed | 40-80cm ↑ | 🔺 🔻

| 1 | 2 | 3 | 4 | 5 | 6 | 7 | 8 | 9 | 10 | 11 | 12 |

Gladiolus palustris GAUD.
Gladiolus palustris

IRIDACEAE

A plant which more or less resembles G. italicus, usually with 3 leaves and reaching a height of up to 50cm. The flowers are arranged in a loose ear-like spike, pink in colour, and all orientated in the same direction; the lower tepals are larger. As its name suggests, this plant prefers damp locations.

G. illyricus is similar, but the lower tepals are smaller and have white shading.

Macedonia, Thrace | 20-50cm ↑ |

| 1 | 2 | 3 | 4 | 5 | 6 | 7 | 8 | 9 | 10 | 11 | 12 |

Gynandriris / Hermodactylus / Iris

The irises take their name from the goddess who carried messages between gods and mortals and used the rainbow as a bridge between the sky and the earth. These beautiful flowers have some notable characteristics. The perianth consists of two types of 'petals'. The three external ones, which are larger, are spreading or drooping and in reality replace the calyx, since here there is no clear distinction between the calyx and corolla. The three internal ones are smaller, erect, and constitute real 'petals'. The style, which resembles the other parts of the perianth, is also divided into three parts and encloses the stamens. This multitude of components, together with their usually strong colouring, produces a flower which is very attractive both to humans and insects. The little bristles on the outer petals are also typical and are used to help support insects which visit the flower.

Gynandriris monophylla BOISS. & HELDR.
Gynandriris monophylla

IRIDACEAE

| 1 | 2 | 3 | 4 | 5 | 6 | 7 | 8 | 9 | 10 | 11 | 12 |

This is undoubtedly the smallest of the irises with a perianth which does not exceed 2cm. The flowers are usually light blue or violet, the three external parts with a yellow fleck surrounded by white. There is only one leaf – hence the name; the latter is dart-shaped with a length which can reach to 30cm. Found in stony locations and phrygana. The name of this genus originates from the Greek words 'gyní' and 'ándras' ('woman and man'), and refers to the reproductive organs of the plant - the style and stamens - which are joined.

Distributed | Up to 5cm ↑ |

Gynandriris sisyrinchium (L.) Parl.   IRIDACEAE
Barbary nut

This plant grows from a bulb, and is a perennial with flowers similar to those of G. monophylla but larger, with a diameter of up to 5cm; they have a short life. There is a fleck on the external parts of the perianth, white or yellow, with violet stippling. The stems are erect with 1-6 flowers and dart-shaped leaves, fluted and with a length that can reach to 50cm. Found in fields and phrygana. The name originates from Theophrastus and probably refers to the membranous spathe, since the ancient Greek word for the leather *chiton* or tunic was *sísurna*.

Distributed | 10-40cm ↑ | ▲ ⚓   1 2 3 4 5 6 7 8 9 10 11 12

Hermodactylus tuberosus (L.) Miller   IRIDACEAE
Snake's head or Widow iris

A plant resembling the iris. It has an erect stem, square in cross-section, with leaves which are a little longer. There is only one flower, yellowish-green with the edges of the external parts of the perianth a velvety mauve. Found in stony places, olive groves, phrygana and fields.
The name of the plant comes from the Greek *Ermés* (*Hermes*) and *dáktylos* (finger), the latter referring to the shape and size of the root. The use of the god's name, however, probably has something to do with the general appearance and strange colouring of the plant, which could recall the wand with the snakes that was the symbol of Hermes.

Distributed | 20-40cm ↑ | ▲ ⚓   1 2 3 4 5 6 7 8 9 10 11 12

Iris attica Boiss. & Hledr.

IRIDACEAE

Iris attica

A small perennial plant; the leaves are grey, lanceolate and have a strong curvature. The flowers may be violet-blue or yellow. The external parts of the perianth are drooping, with dense hair at the centre. The internal parts are large, butterfly-shaped, and erect. Found in stony locations in the mountain zone.

Attica, Thessaly, Peloponnese, Sterea | 5-15cm ↑ | ▲ 🌱 🌿 | 1 2 3 4 5 6 7 8 9 10 11 12

Iris cretensis Poir. / syn. *Iris unguicularis* ssp. *cretensis*

IRIDACEAE

Iris cretensis

The Cretan iris is a perennial with short stems and many straight, narrow leaves which resemble grass. It is one of the most beautiful irises. It forms clumps with many violet flowers which bear impressive white and yellow patterns. Found in open, stony locations, in phrygana, and on slopes.

I. unguicularis is still found in the Peloponnese and in mainland Greece, the Ionian Islands, and Rhodes.

Crete | Up to 20cm ↑ | ▲ 🌿 🌱 | 1 2 3 4 5 6 7 8 9 10 11 12

Iris germanica L.
Iris germanica

A perennial plant with a strong stem that can reach to 1 metre in height. It has large leaves, sword-like and slightly shorter than the stem. The flower is fragrant, up to 10cm, blue-violet with yellow stripes in the centre and white hairs. It is widely cultivated as a decorative plant, often self-sowing.

I. albicans is a similar plant, but smaller in size and with white flowers. It is often self-sowing in ditches and on the edges of fields, near to settlements.

Distributed | Up to 1m ↑ | ▲ ↓ ✿ ✿ | 1 2 3 4 5 6 7 8 9 10 11 12

Iris pseudacorus L.
Yellow flag

This is a tall perennial with leaves that reach the same height as the stem. The flowers are large and yellow, with the external parts of the perianth much larger than the internal ones. The name refers to *Acorus calamus*, with which it is often confused, since its leaves are similar and it prefers the same biotopes. Found in marshes and damp places.

Distributed | Up to 1m ↑ | ▲ ↓ ✿ | 1 2 3 4 5 6 7 8 9 10 11 12

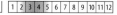

Iris reichenbachii HEUFFEL IRIDACEAE
Iris reichenbachii

This beautiful iris which is found in northern Greece and the Balkans is a perennial with leaves resembling those of *I. attica* and a spathe which is double, green, and has reddish-brown lips. The flowers are light yellow or blue-violet; the external parts are densely haired at the centre and turned downwards, while the internal ones are larger, erect and have spots on the underside. Found in mountain pastures.

Macedonia, Thessaly | 20-40cm ↑ | ▲ ↓

| 1 | 2 | 3 | 4 | 5 | 6 | 7 | 8 | 9 | 10 | 11 | 12 |

Romulea bulbocodium (L.) SEBAST. & MAURI IRIDACEAE
Romulea bulbocodium

This beautiful plant, which grows from a bulb and resembles the crocus, is easily differentiated by the existence of a flower-stem (not found in the crocus) and the absence of a white line on its narrow leaves. The flowers are up to 3cm in diameter with lanceolate, white tepals, a yellow throat and violet 'brush-strokes'. Found in stony locations and phrygana.

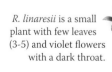

R. linaresii is a small plant with few leaves (3-5) and violet flowers with a dark throat.

Distributed | Up to 10cm ↑ | ▲ ↓

| 1 | 2 | 3 | 4 | 5 | 6 | 7 | 8 | 9 | 10 | 11 | 12 |

LILIACEAE

Allium

Allium is the Latin word for garlic. These are plants which grow from bulbs with basal leaves and a stem that is usually long and, at its tip, has a head covered by a membranous spathe which splits open to reveal a globular umbel containing many flowers. The corolla is star-shaped or bell-shaped and divided into six parts (tepals). There are six stamens. More than 40 varieties of garlic and onion grow in Greece, among which there are the cultivated ones grown as crops. Quite a number of the wild species are endemic.

Allium ampeloprasum L.

Wild leek, great round-headed garlic

The wild leek is a tall plant with narrow leaves, toothed near the stem, becoming narrower towards the tip. The umbel is up to 8cm in diameter with a multitude of pinkish-red flowers and a strong aroma of garlic. The stamens are shorter than the tepals. It is considered to be the progenitor of the cultivated leek. Usually found in abandoned fields and on roadsides.

Distributed | 50-150cm ↑ | 🏔 🌱 📖

| 1 | 2 | 3 | 4 | 5 | 6 | 7 | 8 | 9 | 10 | 11 | 12 |

• *Allium heldreichii* Boiss.

Allium heldreichii

This endemic A*llium* has a slender stem and oblong, concave leaves. The umbel contains deep pink flowers with dark veining and stamens shorter than the perianth. Found in rocky areas in the mountain zone.

Macedonia, Thessaly | 20-40cm ↑ | 🏔 🌱

| 1 | 2 | 3 | 4 | 5 | 6 | 7 | 8 | 9 | 10 | 11 | 12 |

Allium neapolitanum Cyr.

LILIACEAE

Naples garlic

This has a characteristic triangular stem with one ridge slightly less angular than the other two, and 2-3 smooth leaves. The umbel is loose and up to 10cm in diameter, with white flowers on long stalks. The stamens are shorter than the tepals. The plant is common, with a very wide distribution.

Allium subhirsutum is similar, but differs in that it is smaller in size, and has a cylindrical stem and hairy leaves.

Distributed | 20-50cm ↑ | △ ⚓ 🌿

1	2	3	4	5	6	7	8	9	10	11	12

Allium nigrum L.

LILIACEAE

Allium nigrum

A perennial with leaves that are long and have a width of up to 8cm. The umbel is globular with a diameter of up to 10cm, containing many pink or white flowers with green veining on the outer side. The stamens are a little shorter than the tepals. Found in fields, olive groves, and on roadsides.

Peloponnese, Aegean, Rhodes, Crete | 40-100cm ↑ | △ ⚓ 🌿

1	2	3	4	5	6	7	8	9	10	11	12

Allium roseum L.

Rose garlic

This very beautiful *Allium* has 2-5 fluted leaves that are smooth and slightly toothed. The umbel is globular and up to 7cm with many (up to 30) pink flowers on short stalks. The stamens are longer than the tepals. Found in fields, ditches, and on roadsides.

Distributed | 50-80cm ↑ | ⛰

| 1 | 2 | 3 | 4 | 5 | 6 | 7 | 8 | 9 | 10 | 11 | 12 |

● *Androcymbium rechingeri* GREUTER

Androcymbium rechingeri

This beautiful, endemic little lily flowers in the midst of winter. It has a very short stem and elongated, lanceolate, smooth leaves up to 15cm in length. The flowers have a diameter of 3-5cm, with lanceolate tepals, white with pink veining. It is considered to be among the rarest plants in Greece, found in sandy locations on the little islet of Elafónisos and at Falásarna in western Crete.

Crete | Up to 10cm ↑ | ⛰ ↡ ⬥

| 1 | 2 | 3 | 4 | 5 | 6 | 7 | 8 | 9 | 10 | 11 | 12 |

Anthericum liliago L.

St. Bernards's lily

LILIACEAE

An elegant, perennial plant similar to *Lilium*, hence its name. It has an erect, smooth stem, and narrow, linear leaves which sometimes reach the height of the stem. The flowers are on a thin stalk and in a loose raceme on the upper part of the stem. The tepals are white, three-veined and have a length of up to 2cm. Found in pastures and stony locations in the mountain zone.

Thrace, Macedonia, Epirus, Thessaly, Peloponnese | 20-80cm ↑ | ▲ ⚘ | 1 2 3 4 **5 6** 7 8 9 10 11 12

Asparagus aphyllus L.

Asparagus aphyllus

LILIACEAE

A spiny, often climbing and much-branched phrygano plant in which the leaves have been replaced by spiny, infertile branchlets which grow in clusters. The flowers are yellowish-green, fleshy and in small groups. The wild asparagus is edible; the tender tips of the stems are gathered and considered a choice dish. Found in olive groves, hedgerows, and phrygana.

Distributed | 0.50-1m ↑ | ▲ ✦ ‖ | 1 2 3 4 5 6 **7 8 9** 10 11 12

Asphodeline lutea (L.) RCHB.

LILIACEAE

Yellow asphodel

A perennial plant with an erect stem and many narrow leaves along almost its whole length; this is a characteristic which differentiates it from the asphodel. The flowers are yellow in a dense raceme at the tip of the stem. The plant often forms large communities and it is in one such meadow, in Hades, according to Homer, that the souls of the Dead are gathered. The tender stems of the plant are edible. Found in infertile, stony locations and in phrygana.

Distributed | 0.50-1.20m ↑ | 🏔 🐾 ⚑ | 1 2 3 **4** 5 6 7 8 9 10 11 12

Asphodeline liburnica (SCOP.) RCHB.

LILIACEAE

Asphodeline liburnica

A delicate, perennial plant with narrow, linear leaves which reach to the middle of the stem. The flowers are yellow, almost similar to those of *A. lutea* but arranged in a much looser spike. Found in stony locations and abandoned fields.

Distributed | 20-60cm ↑ | 🏔 🐾 | 1 2 3 4 5 **6** 7 8 9 10 11 12

Asphodelus aestivus Brot.
Common asphodel

This is the most common of the asphodels. It is a perennial with a cylindrical, hollow stem, branching at the tip. The leaves are elongated and triangular; in contrast to those of *Asphodeline*, they are all concentrated at the base of the stem. The flowers have white tepals with russet veining in the centre, and are in terminal racemes. Found in infertile, stony locations, often in large populations.

A. albus (white asphodel), which is not found on the islands, is similar in appearance but has linear leaves and the stripes on the flowers are in shades of green.

Distributed | 0.50-1.25m ↑ |

1	2	3	4	5	6	7	8	9	10	11	12

Asphodelus fistulosus L.
Hollow-leaved asphodel

A more delicate plant than A. aestivus, with many slender, hollow (empty) stems. The leaves are narrow and straight, all concentrated at the base of the stem. The flowers are white or slightly shaded with pink, with brownish veining at the centre of the tepals, in a loose raceme. The fruits, as in the other varieties of *Asphodelus* and *Asphodeline,* are round berries. Found in barren, stony locations.

Distributed | 20-60cm ↑ |

1	2	3	4	5	6	7	8	9	10	11	12

● *Chionodoxa nana* Boiss. & Heldr. / syn. *Scilla nana*   LILIACEAE
Chionodoxa nana

This little plant with its blindingly blue flower has perhaps the most beautiful name in the world – and this is not by pure chance, since it often appears like a surprise from out of the snow. It grows from a bulb and has a slender stem, up to 20cm, and elongated, lanceolate and fluted leaves. The flowers are blue, white at the centre, and have a diameter of up to 4cm. Found in the mountain and alpine zone in the mountains of Crete.

Crete | 5-20cm ↑ | 1 2 3 4 5 6 7 8 9 10 11 12

Colchicum

These beautiful, little pink lilies grow from bulbs; they resemble the crocuses in appearance, although they are not connected to them in any way. In the colchicum, a tubular stem springs from the bulb and is surrounded by a spathe. At the tip of the tube there develops the flower, with a perianth divided into 6 tepals. There are six stamens with anthers supported at the centre. The leaves usually appear before flowering. Most of the more than twenty varieties of colchicum which grow in Greece are autumn-flowering. All of the parts of the plant are poisonous, due to the presence of colchicine, a potent toxin. It was with this poison that Medea killed her children in Colchis; the plant was given the name *colchicum*.

● *Colchicum cretense* Greuter   LILIACEAE
Colchicum cretense

The Cretan colchicum is a dwarf plant with flowers ranging from pink to almost white, and tepals up to 2cm. The leaves appear after flowering, which takes place in autumn. The plant is endemic to the great mountain massifs of Crete.

Crete | 5-10cm ↑ | 1 2 3 4 5 6 7 8 9 10 11 12

Colchicum macrophyllum B.L. Burtt

LILIACEAE

Colchicum macrophyllum

One of the most beautiful of the colchicums, with large, elegant flowers decorated with pink spots like a mosaic. It flowers early in autumn and prefers fertile, shaded soil in pine forests and olive groves. The tepals are more than 5cm long. The leaves are very large, up to 30cm – hence the name – and are produced in spring.

Crete, Dodecanese | Up to 30cm ↑

Colchicum pusillum Sieber

LILIACEAE

Colchicum pusillum

A very small plant with flowers in a variety of pink tones; up to 4 flowers grow from every bulb. The anthers are yellow. The lanceolate leaves appear together with the flowers in autumn. Found in open stony locations and in loose phrygana thickets.

C. cupani is similar, with a distribution that reaches as far as Epirus. It differs in its leaves, which are broader, and in the anthers, which are darker.

Cyclades, Dodecanese, Crete | Up to 10cm ↑

Colchicum bivonae Guss.

This is quite similar in appearance to *C. macrophyllum*, but its tepals close in towards the middle, so that the shape of the flower resembles that of a cup. There are up to 9 leaves, elongated, lanceolate and smooth; they appear in spring. The flower blooms in autumn with a strong pink, rhomboid blazon. Found in shady, stony locations.

Epirus | Up to 30cm ↑ | ⛰ ⚐ ☠

| 1 | 2 | 3 | 4 | 5 | 6 | 7 | 8 | 9 | 10 | 11 | 12 |

Fritillaria

These plants grow from bulbs. They have narrow, lanceolate leaves and a bell-shaped flower, consisting of 6 tepals. The shape of the flower and the square blazon patterns which they have on the exterior recall the *fritillus*, a cup used by the Romans to throw dice. The Fritillaria, with their drooping heads and their distinctive colouring, could be characterized as poor relations of the tulips, but they nevertheless have a particular beauty of their own which stems from their fragile elegance. More than 20 species are found in Greece.

● *Fritillaria graeca* Boiss. & Spruner

Fritillaria graeca

The leaves are greyish-green and lanceolate, the lower ones quite broad, the upper ones narrower. The tepals are dark brownish-red with a light-green line at the centre. The anthers are yellow. Found in open rocky locations, in phrygana, and in pine forests.

Epirus, Thessaly, Sterea, Peloponnese, Crete | 20-30cm ↑ | ⛰ ⚐

| 1 | 2 | 3 | 4 | 5 | 6 | 7 | 8 | 9 | 10 | 11 | 12 |

● *Fritillaria messanensis* Raf. LILIACEAE

Fritillaria messanensis

A delicately-built plant with very narrow greyish leaves, the lower ones arranged singly and alternate, and the upper ones in whorls of three. There are 1-2 flowers, more or less similar to those of *F. graeca* but with stronger blazon patterns and lips slightly turned outwards. The anthers are yellow. Usually found in open phrygana.

Peloponnese, Crete | 15-40cm ↑ | ▲ ↯

1 2 **3 4 5** 6 7 8 9 10 11 12

Fritillaria pontica Wahlenb. LILIACEAE

Fritillaria pontica

The leaves are light green and lanceolate, arranged similarly to those of *F. messanensis*. The flowers are yellowish-green with brown shading at the base and on the lips. The anthers are yellow. Every tepal has a characteristic black spot on the inside, which facilitates recognition of the plant.

Thrace, Macedonia, Lesbos | Up to 40cm ↑ | ▲ ↯

1 2 3 **4 5** 6 7 8 9 10 11 12

Fritillaria rhodia A. Hansen

Fritillaria rhodia

Quite a number of islands in the Aegean, such as Chios, the Sporades, Spetses, Evvia and Rhodes, have their own endemic fritillaria. *F. rhodia* is distinguished by its linear, twisted leaves and the yellow-green, oblong flower. The fleshy tepals are slightly inclined outwards, which gives the plant elegance; it prefers pine forests.

Rhodes, Epirus | Up to 30cm ↑ |

1 2 3 4 5 6 7 8 9 10 11 12

Gagea graeca L.

Gagea graeca

This is distinguished from other varieties of gagea by its white, bell-shaped flower. It is a perennial with slender, well-bent stems and dart-shaped leaves, most of them basal. There are up to three flowers, six-part and with dark veining. Found in areas of phrygana and stony places.

S. Greece, Aegean, Crete | 5-25cm ↑ |

1 2 3 4 5 6 7 8 9 10 11 12

Gagea peduncularis (J. & Presl) Pasch.

Gagea peduncularis

A small, perennial, downy plant with short stems. The upper leaves are lanceolate, the lower leaves – of which there are always 2 – are linear and fluted. The flowers are yellow, greenish on the exterior, solitary and have a diameter of up to 2.5cm. Found in thickets, phrygana, and open stony locations.

Many other species, such as *G. bohemica*, are similar but exhibit little differences in their leaves and the shape of the tepals.

Distributed | Up to 15cm ↑ |

1 2 3 4 5 6 7 8 9 10 11 12

Lilium

Among the most impressive and beautiful plants of the Greek landscape, the lilies are avidly collected with the result that in some areas they are threatened with disappearance. For example *L. candidum* - the Madonna lily - was once profuse on Crete but has now almost disappeared. Thes plants grow from a bulb with very characteristic flowers whose perianth is separated into 6 glistening, waxy parts (tepals), turned backwards. Five species are met in Greece, most of them in the north of the country.

Lilium candidum L.

LILIACEAE

Madonna lily

The stem of this plant has leaves all along its length; the lower ones are larger and can reach 30cm in length, while the upper leaves are much smaller. There are more than 10 flowers on the upper part of the stem; they are white, fragrant and up to 8cm long with tepals turned outwards. *L. candidum* is the lily of the Evangelium, and for that reason called the 'Madonna lily'. Frescoes depicting lilies at the Minoan palaces of Crete indicate that the Minoans probably cultivated them as decorative plants; they are widely grown for this purpose today.

Macedonia, Epirus, Thessaly, Sterea, Peloponnese, Crete | Up to 1m ↑ | 🏔 🌱 🌿 | 1 2 3 4 **5 6** 7 8 9 10 11 12

Lilium martagon L.

LILIACEAE

Martagon lily

1 2 3 4 5 **6 7 8** 9 10 11 12

This plant can reach a height of 1.5 metres. It has lanceolate leaves, arranged in whorls along the length of the stem. There are many nodding flowers with a diameter which can reach to 7cm, concentrated in the upper part of the stem. The perianth has tepals that are strongly turned backwards, deep red or flesh-coloured. Found from Thrace to central Greece, it flowers in the summer. The name has a Turkish root and means 'turban'; it is an entirely apt description of the plant.

Thessaly, Macedonia, Thrace, Epirus, Sterea, Evvia | 0,50-1,50m ↑ | 🏔 🌱 🌿

Lilium rhodopaeum Delip.

Lilium rhodopaeum

A very exquisite lily, endemic to
the Rhodopi mountain chain.
It has a strong, erect stem and
linear-lanceolate leaves, alternating along the whole length of the
stem. There is usually one flower,
which is yellow and has a diameter of up to 12cm with sections
of the perianth turned backwards
in an almost complete circle.
There are 6 stamens with orange-
red anthers. The plant, which is
found in alpine forests, has been
characterized as 'vulnerable'.

L. albanicum also has yellow flowers
and is found in the northern Pindos
Mountains.

Lilium chalcedonicum L.

This plant has many lanceolate leaves
along the whole length of its spotted
stem. There are up to seven flowers with a
diameter of 4cm, deep red in colour with
tepals turned backwards, almost in a full
circle. Its distribution is from northern
Greece to the Peloponnese, with a preference for mountainous forest locations. It
flowers in the summer.

Thrace | Up to 1m↑ |

| 1 | 2 | 3 | 4 | 5 | 6 | 7 | 8 | 9 | 10 | 11 | 12 |

Muscari commutatum GUSS.

LILIACEAE

Dark grape hyacinth

The Muscari are perennial, herbaceous plants with all their leaves concentrated at the base and flowers which are usually ovoid or cylindrical in shape, narrowing towards the toothed lip, and arranged in a terminal raceme. More than 10 varieties are found in Greece, some of them endemic.

M. commutatum has linear, fluted leaves, and a dense flower-spike, ovoid with dark blue-violet flowers. Found in stony locations, pine forests and on the slopes at the sides of roads.

Distributed, excluding Crete | 10-20cm ↑ | ▲ ⤵

| 1 | 2 | 3 | 4 | 5 | 6 | 7 | 8 | 9 | 10 | 11 | 12 |

Muscari comosum (L.) MILL.

LILIACEAE

Tassel hyacinth

This is the most common of the *Muscari* and has concave leaves that are up to 3cm wide and 40cm long. The lower section of the raceme is loose and consists of brown flowers, while the upper section is denser with blue-violet flowers. The upper flowers are sterile. Found in fields, often in large populations. The bulbs of *M. comosum* constitute an excellent appetizer known as *skordouláki*, especially on Crete.

Distributed | 15-50cm ↑ | ▲ ⤵ ⏚

| 1 | 2 | 3 | 4 | 5 | 6 | 7 | 8 | 9 | 10 | 11 | 12 |

Muscari neglectum Guss. ex ten. / syn. *Muscari racemosum*   LILIACEAE
Common grape hyacinth

This plant has narrow, cylindrical and ridged leaves which are longer than the stem. The flowers are arranged in a raceme, and are light or dark blue; they more or less resemble those of *M. commutatum*, but have a white, toothed lip. Found in rocky locations and abandoned fields.

Distributed | Up to 30cm ↑ | ▲ ⚓

| 1 | 2 | 3 | 4 | 5 | 6 | 7 | 8 | 9 | 10 | 11 | 12 |

Ornithogalum

The ornithogala are elegant plants, growing from bulbs, which have white, star-like flowers. They retain their ancient Greek name of 'bird's milk' from *órnis* (bird) and *gála* (milk); the expression 'tou poulioú to gála' is used to refer to 'abundance' but here the name is probably connected with the white colour of the tepals, which in fact are usually green on the outside with a white border. More than 20 species are found in Greece, some of which have greenish flowers, such as the endemic *O. creticum*.

● *Ornithogalum atticum* Boiss.   LILIACEAE
Ornithogalum atticum

This is a plant of small stature with a short stem from which the longer flower-stalks develop in a cluster. It is easily recognised by the broad, prostrate leaves which are of a length equal to the height of the plant. The flowers have a diameter of up to 4cm and are arranged in a loose inflorescence. Found in open, stony locations.

Attica, Evvia | 5-20cm ↑ | ▲ ⚓ ☠

| 1 | 2 | 3 | 4 | 5 | 6 | 7 | 8 | 9 | 10 | 11 | 12 |

Ornithogalum narbonense L. / syn. *Ornithogalum pyramidale* LILIACEAE
Ornithogalum narbonense

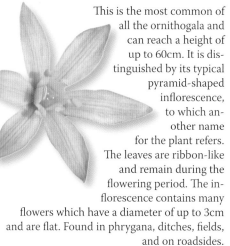

This is the most common of all the ornithogala and can reach a height of up to 60cm. It is distinguished by its typical pyramid-shaped inflorescence, to which another name for the plant refers. The leaves are ribbon-like and remain during the flowering period. The inflorescence contains many flowers which have a diameter of up to 3cm and are flat. Found in phrygana, ditches, fields, and on roadsides.

Distributed | Up to 60cm ↑ |

| 1 | 2 | 3 | 4 | 5 | 6 | 7 | 8 | 9 | 10 | 11 | 12 |

Ornithogalum nutans L. LILIACEAE
Drooping Star of Bethlehem

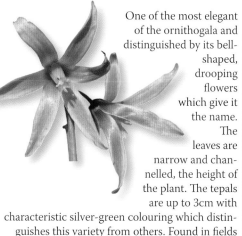

One of the most elegant of the ornithogala and distinguished by its bell-shaped, drooping flowers which give it the name. The leaves are narrow and channelled, the height of the plant. The tepals are up to 3cm with characteristic silver-green colouring which distinguishes this variety from others. Found in fields and phrygana, usually in the mountain zone.

Distributed | 20-60cm ↑ |

| 1 | 2 | 3 | 4 | 5 | 6 | 7 | 8 | 9 | 10 | 11 | 12 |

Ruscus aculeatus L.

Butcher's broom

This is a beautiful, decorative shrub, which often confuses those who see it because it appears to produce fruits from the leaves. In reality however, what look like leaves are only leaf-shaped, leathery branchlets, barbed at the tip (*aculeus* = barbed).The flowers are stalkless and appear on the branchlets in the spring, to be followed in summer by cherry-like fruits. Found in shaded locations and forested areas.

Distributed | Up to 1m ↑ | | 1 2 3 4 5 6 7 8 9 10 11 12

Scilla autumnalis L.

Autumn squill

As its name suggests, this little squill flowers in the autumn. It is a perennial plant that grows from a bulb with an erect stem and linear, smooth leaves which appear after flowering, all basal. The flowers are small, 1cm at the most, with slender stalks; they are pink, blue or violet with black anthers. The spike consists of a pyramidal raceme at the end of the stem. Found in rocky locations, on slopes, in phrygana and on roadsides.

Distributed | 5-30cm ↑ | | 1 2 3 4 5 6 7 8 9 10 11 12

Scilla bifolia L.

LILIACEAE

Alpine squill

A delicate perennial plant, growing from a bulb, with an erect, russet-coloured stem. The leaves are linear, up to 1cm in width, grow from the root and are longer than the stem and nearly always 2 in number. The flowers are up to 1.5cm, blue with long stalks in a loose raceme. This is the wild hyacinth of Theophrastus. Found in shady, forested locations and meadows in the mountain zone, and also cultivated for decoration.

Distributed | 10-20cm ↑ | 🏔 🌿 🌱 | 1 2 3 **4 5** 6 7 8 9 10 11 12

Smilax aspera L.

LILIACEAE

Common smilax

A climbing plant, common in hedgerows and thickets. It has a spiny stem, square in cross-section, and can reach a great height. The leaves are dart- to heart-shaped, smooth and leathery with two tendrils at the base of the leaf-stalk. The flowers are fragrant, light-coloured in shades of pink, yellow and green, in hanging inflorescences. The plant is unisexual, i.e. male and female flowers are found on different plants. The fruits are red berries arranged in bunches, and very decorative.

Distributed | Up to 15m ↑ → | 🏔 🌿 🏺 | 1 2 3 4 5 6 **7 8 9 10** 11 12

Tulipa bakeri A.D. HALL

LILIACEAE

Tulipa bakeri

| 1 | 2 | 3 | 4 | 5 | 6 | 7 | 8 | 9 | 10 | 11 | 12 |

This beautiful tulip covers the fields of the Omalos High Plateau on Crete in spring with its multicoloured flowers. The tepals are 4-5cm in length, yellow at the base, white at the centre and pink at the tip, the latter colour predominating. The anthers are yellow. The leaves are concentrated at the base of the stem, elongated, lanceolate and fluted. The plant is endemic to Crete.

Crete | 20-40cm ↑

Tulipa doerfleri GAND.
Tulipa doerfleri

This endemic tulip is found mainly on the little mountain plateau of 'Yous Kámbos' in central Crete. The petals are 3-4cm, narrowing to a point at the tip; they are red, often with yellow shading on the outside. The anthers are blackish-red, and the leaves narrow, elongated and ridged.

Similar to *T. doerfleri* and without clear distinguishing features, are *T. orphanidea* which grows in the Peloponnese, and *T. Hageri* which is found in central mainland Greece.

Tulipa goulimyi
This endemic plant greatly resembles *T. doerfleri* but differs in that has very billowy leaves. Found in phrygana, often near the sea.

Crete | 10-30cm ↑ | 1 2 3 **4 5 6** 7 8 9 10 11 12

Tulipa saxatilis SIEBER EX SPRENGEL
Rock tulip

There are no clear botanical differences between this plant and *T. bakeri*; it differs in the colour of the anthers, which here are black or brown. Found in various biotopes from rocky slopes to uncultivated fields and the sides of streams. It is often met at low altitudes; this also differentiates it from *T. bakeri* which prefers altitudes of above 800 metres.

Crete, Aegean, Rhodes | Up to 30cm ↑ | 1 2 **3 4 5** 6 7 8 9 10 11 12

Urginea maritima L. (Baker) / syn. *Drimia maritima* LILIACEAE
Sea squill

A common, widely distributed perennial plant with a large, bulky bulb which can reach up to 15cm in diameter. The leaves are smooth, broad, and lanceolate and appear in spring, while by the middle of summer, shortly before flowering, they have already disappeared. The flower-bearing stem is russet-coloured, erect, slender and leafless. The flowers are very many in number, in a dense elongated spike; the tepals are white with a pink vein. It is considered a symbol of good luck and for this reason even today is hung at doors of houses at the time of the New Year. It is a poisonous plant; however, it has a great number of medicinal uses. Despite its name, it is found all the way up to the mountain zone in stony and barren locations, phrygana, oak forests and olive groves.

Distributed | Up to 1m ↑

| 1 | 2 | 3 | 4 | 5 | 6 | 7 | 8 | 9 | 10 | 11 | 12 |

ORCHIDACEAE

More than one hundred species of orchid are found in Greece, excluding those of the genus *Ophrys* of which there are the same number again. These very beautiful plants have some commmon characteristics. The flower, which is symmetrical on the axis (zygomorphic) consists of three sepals, two lateral and one central (dorsal). In front of the latter, two petals cover the reproductive organs of the plant, while a third petal, larger and different to the others, extends forwards to form that which is designated as the lip. The latter, more or less, determines the appearance of the flower, since it may be entire or divided into lobes, and may or may not bear a pattern. At the base of the lip in some species there is the entrance to the spur which carries the nectar, in order to attract pollinators, while in other species the shapes of the lip are those which attract the insects, a technique which is used to a certain extent by the genus *Ophrys*.

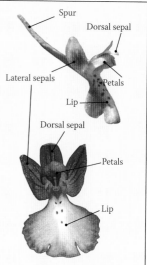

Spur · Dorsal sepal · Lateral sepals · Petals · Lip · Dorsal sepal · Petals · Lip

Aceras anthropophorum (L.) W.T. Aiton

Man orchid

ORCHIDACEAE

A very individual-looking, dainty plant with a dense ear-like inflorescence and flowers with a lip divided into four straight lobes which make it look like a little man – hence its name (*ánthropos*= man, *féro*= to bear). Its colouring varies from russet to greenish-yellow, while the absence of a spur is characteristic. The leaves are concentrated in a rosette at the base of the plant. It is mainly found in phrygana thickets.

Distributed | Up to 30cm ↑ |

1 2 3 4 5 6 7 8 9 10 11 12

Anacamptis pyramidalis (L.) Rich.
Pyramidal orchid

This is one of the more common orchids, and a unique representative of its genus. The name comes from the Greek word *anakámpto*, meaning 'to turn/bend backwards', and probably refers to the the long, slender spur which is turned upwards. The plant has a slender stem and very characteristic pyramid-shaped flower-spike with white or pink flowers, their lip divided into three equal lobes. The leaves are concentrated at the base and have almost withered by the time of flowering. Usually found in phrygana.

Distributed | 15- 40cm ↑ | ▲ ↓ | 1 | 2 | 3 | 4 | 5 | 6 | 7 | 8 | 9 | 10 | 11 | 12 |

Barlia robertiana (Loisel.) Greuter
Robert's giant orchid

This orchid is undoubtedly the largest in height, often reaching to over 50cm, with large leaves that are often rolled around the brownish stem. The flowers are arranged in a dense spike in a variety of colours and shades, from red and white to green. The lip is trilobate, often with spotting; the side lobes are undulating, the middle one is divided. Found in phrygana, stony locations, and olive groves.

Distributed | 30-70cm ↑ | ▲ ↓ | 1 | 2 | 3 | 4 | 5 | 6 | 7 | 8 | 9 | 10 | 11 | 12 |

Cephalanthera cucullata Boiss. & Heldr.   ORCHIDACEAE
Hooded cephalanthera

The cephalanthera or helleborines are elegant perennial orchids which took their name from the Greek
words *kefáli* and *anther*, meaning 'head' and
'flower' respectively; these probably refer
to the shape of the flower. *C. cucullata* ia a
rare endemic species with a very limited
occurrence on the three great mountains
of Crete and considered to be threatened
with extinction. It does not exceed 30cm
in height and is smaller than the other
varieties of cephalanthera. It has white
or whitish-pink flowers in a relatively
dense spike with the bracts covering the
flowers like a hood. It has a small
spur and is the only
cephalanthera to ex-
hibit this charac-
teristic. Found
in phrygana,
forests and shady,
cool locations.

Crete | Up to 30cm ↑ | 〰 ⚘

1 2 3 4 5 6 7 8 9 10 11 12

Cephalanthera longifolia (L.) Fritsch.   ORCHIDACEAE
Long or sword-leaved cephalanthera

The most common type
of cephalanthera and easily
distinguished by the oblong,
alternate leaves which cover the
stem along most of its length.
The flowers are white, normally
closed and with very short
bracts, in a loose inflorescence.
A particular characteristic is the
yellow fleck on the edge of the
lip. Found in forests and thickets in the mountain zone.

C. damasonium also ▶
has white flowers but is
differentiated by its large, ovate
leaves and larger bracts.

© Z.A.

Distributed | Up to 30cm ↑ | 〰 ⚘

1 2 3 4 5 6 7 8 9 10 11 12

Cephalanthera rubra (L.) L.C.M.Richard

ORCHIDACEAE

Red helleborine

This is the only non-white cephalanthera and is distinguished immediately by its particularly pinkish-violet colour. It has oblong, fluted leaves, pointed at the tip, and a loose spike with rather open flowers. Found more often in northern Greece, in forests in the alpine zone.

Distributed | 20-60cm ↑ |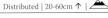

| 1 | 2 | 3 | 4 | 5 | 6 | 7 | 8 | 9 | 10 | 11 | 12 |

Dactylorhiza cordigera (Fries) Soó

ORCHIDACEAE

Dactylorhiza cordigera

The dactylorhizae are amongst the most beautiful of the orchids and their name originates from the Greek words *dáktylos* and *ríza*, meaning 'finger' and 'root' respectively, and naturally referring to the shape of the root. *D. cordigera* is a relatively small plant with lanceolate leaves, speckled on both sides. The flowers are purple-violet in a dense ear-spike at the tip of the stem. The plant takes its name from the heart-shaped lip which also has similar patterns. Found in damp locations in the mountain zone.

Thrace, Macedonia, Epirus | 15-30cm ↑ |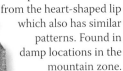

| 1 | 2 | 3 | 4 | 5 | 6 | 7 | 8 | 9 | 10 | 11 | 12 |

Dactylorhiza romana (Sebast.) Soó

Roman cuckoo flower, Roman orchid

This has lanceolate leaves concentrated in a rosette at the base of the plant. The flowers may be purple, ochre-white or white and have long spurs which are turned upwards, a characteristic which differentiates the plant from the similar-looking *D. sambucina*. Found in forest clearings, olive groves, thickets and phrygana.

◀*D. sambucina*, found in northern Greece, has similar characteristics, but the flowers have a fatter spur, turned downwards.

Distributed | 10-40cm ↑ | ▲ ⚓ | 1 2 3 4 5 6 7 8 9 10 11 12

Dactylorhiza saccifera (Brongniart) Soó

Dactylorhiza saccifera

This plant was named for its characteristic spur, which is short and fat like a sack. It is a slender-bodied plant with large, elongated lanceolate leaves with dark flecks, which cover a large part of the stem. The pinkish-violet flowers are concentrated in a spike at the tip of the stem and apart from the existence of a spur, are further distinguished by the trilobate, spotted lip. A common variety, found in damp clearings in chestnut and beech forests.

Thrace, Macedonia, Epirus, Thessaly. N. Greece | 20-60cm ↑ | ▲ ⚓ | 1 2 3 4 5 6 7 8 9 10 11 12

Himantoglossum caprinum (M.Bieb) Spreng.
ORCHIDACEAE
Himantoglossum caprinum

This impressive orchid which often reaches a height of 1 metre is distinguished by its greenish-red, distinctively-shaped flowers which grow in a loose inflorescence along almost the whole length of the stem. The very characteristic undulating lip is divided into three lobes of which the middle lobe is strap-like and can have a length of up to 10cm. Found in forest clearings in the mountain zone.

◀ The very similar *H. samariense*, which is endemic to the great mountain massifs of Crete, is a slightly smaller plant, and earlier-flowering.

Thrace, Macedonia, Epirus, Thessaly | 30-80cm ↑ | ▲ ⚘   1 2 3 4 5 6 7 8 9 10 11 12

Limodorum abortivum (L.) Swartz
ORCHIDACEAE
Violet limodore, violet bird's nest orchid

The name of this strange but at the same time impressive, slender-bodied orchid comes from the absence of leaves, which gives the impression that the plant has cast them off. Those few leaves that do exist are small and wrapped on the stem. It has large whitish-violet flowers with spreading sepals and a darker lip, curving downwards. It is usually found in pine forests.

Distributed | 30-60cm ↑ | ▲ ⚘   1 2 3 4 5 6 7 8 9 10 11 12

Neotinea maculata (Desf.) Stearn / syn. *Orchis intacta*   ORCHIDACEAE
Dense-flowering orchid

A small, perennial orchid, with leaves in a rosette, the upper ones enclosing the stem. The tiny, anthropomorphic whitish-pink flowers form a dense spike. The sepals and petals form a small dome. The lip is trilobate with the large middle lobe divided at the centre. The flowers, stem and leaves are often spotted, hence the name. Found in pine forests, thickets and phrygana.

Distributed | 10-20cm ↑ |

| 1 | 2 | 3 | 4 | 5 | 6 | 7 | 8 | 9 | 10 | 11 | 12 |

Neottia nidus avis Rich.   ORCHIDACEAE
Bird's nest orchid

This strange orchid is often confused with orobanche both because of its ochre colour and by reason of the absence of leaves which here have been replaced by alternating periblastic scales. The flowers are numerous, in a cluster-like inflorescence, with sepals and petals that are similar and a lip that is longer and two-lobed. Found in shady locations and humus-like soils, often as a parasite. The name refers to the shape of the rhizome, which resembles that of a nest (Latin *nidus* = nest and *avis* = bird).

Thessaly, Macedonia, Epirus, Thrace | 20-40cm ↑ |

| 1 | 2 | 3 | 4 | 5 | 6 | 7 | 8 | 9 | 10 | 11 | 12 |

Ophrys

These little orchids, known not by chance locally as 'little bees', are represented in Greece through more than 80 different species and subspecies. Of particular interest is the shape of the flower of this genus and the way in which insects are attracted for pollination. The flower consists of three sepals, two terminal and one central (dorsal) and three petals, of which the middle one is much larger, usually fleshy, and bears all the patterns and forms which make each species of Ophrys unique. At the base of the lip there is a stigmatic cavity and above it there hang two 'antenna' with sticky tips – the anthers. There is no spur, i.e. nectar-container, and what attracts insects is simply the appearance of the plant, which in each species resembles that of the female of a particular species of insect. This results in the landing of the respective male insect on the lip; in attempting to mate with what appears to be a female, it ruptures the anthers, which adhere to its head. The insect carries them to the next flower, deposits them on the stigma and thus fertilization is accomplished. This 'sexual mimicry' sometimes confuses insects with the result that a multitude of hybrids has come into existence, making the already difficult process of indentification of these unique plants even more problematic.

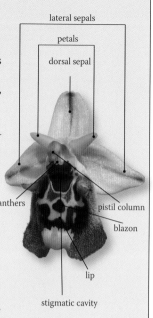

lateral sepals
petals
dorsal sepal
anthers
pistil column
blazon
lip
stigmatic cavity

Ophrys apifera Huds.
Bee orchid

ORCHIDACEAE

This is the only one of all the Greek Ophrys which is self-pollinating – that is, the anthers touch the stigmatic cavity without the help of insects. The protuberance which turns in on itself below the lip and the large and nose-like pistil column are characteristic. The sepals are almost white with green or pink shading. The terminal lobes of the lip are downy. The plant prefers damp meadows.

Distributed | 10-50cm ↑ | 🔺 ⚓

| 1 | 2 | 3 | 4 | 5 | 6 | 7 | 8 | 9 | 10 | 11 | 12 |

Ophrys bombyliflora Link

Bumblebee ophrys

The smaller of the *Ophrys*, this is easily identified by its little flower, which does not exceed 2cm, with the rounded brownish central lobe and smaller, downy lateral lobes. The sepals are round, green and a little larger than the lip. The two petals are the same colour, but with a brownish base. Found in phrygana and olive groves.

Distributed | 10-25cm ↑ |

1 2 3 4 5 6 7 8 9 10 11 12

Ophrys candica Greuter, Matthäs & Risse

ORCHIDACEAE

White ophrys

A relatively rare orchid with a blazon pattern which re-sembles marble. The sepals and petals are light pink, the latter very small. The lip is undivided, downy on the edge, with two little humps at the edges of the blazon. At the centre of the lip there is a little protuberance turned upwards, similar to that of *O. episcopalis*. Found in phrygana and areas of sparse forest.

Rhodes, Crete, Aegean, Peloponnese | 20-30cm ↑ |

1 2 3 4 5 6 7 8 9 10 11 12

Ophrys cretica (Vierh.) E. Nelson
ORCHIDACEAE

Ariadne's ophrys

A polymorphic plant with many subspecies. The petals are oblong and brownish –pink in colour. The lip is almost black, tri-lobate, and slightly downy, with dow-nier side lobes. The blazon is violet with a white pattern in the form of a letter 'H'. Found in phrygana and olive groves.

Crete, Peloponnese, Aegean, Rhodes | 20-30cm ↑ | 🏔 ⚓ | 1 2 3 4 5 6 7 8 9 10 11 12

● *Ophrys episcopalis* Poir.
ORCHIDACEAE

Large-flowered bee ophrys

This plant has an impres-sive, large and undivided lip with its borders turned slightly upwards and humps at the shoulders, which are very downy. At the centre of the lip there is a large protuberance, also turned upwards. The blazon has a yellowish-green pattern. The sepals and petals are pink. *O. episcopalis* is closely re-lated to the *O. holoserica* of central Europe.

Crete, Rhodes, Aegean | 10-40cm ↑ | 🏔 ⚓ | 1 2 3 4 5 6 7 8 9 10 11 12

Ophrys fusca LINK

Sombre bee orchid

A species represented in Greece by four endemic subspecies. Generally, these plants have green sepals and almost straight petals with russet shading. The lip is three-lobed, dark brown, often with yellowish borders. The blazon has metallic brown-blue shading, often framed by a light-coloured 'ω'. Two hump-like swellings at the base of the lip create a little groove which divides the blazon into two. Found usually in phrygana.

Distributed | 10-40cm ↑ |

`1 2 3 4 5 6 7 8 9 10 11 12`

Ophrys heldreichii SCHELTER

Heldreich's ophrys

This plant has an ovate, three-lobed lip. The middle, large lobe has a raised protuberance and side borders turned inwards, this giving it the ovate appearance. The blazon has a leather-like texture and whitish-yellow pattern. The two lateral lobes have noses, and are hairy with strong humps at their base. The sepals and petals are pink. Very frequent in occurrence, found mainly in phrygana.

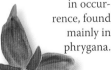

Distributed | Up to 40cm ↑ |

`1 2 3 4 5 6 7 8 9 10 11 12`

Ophrys iricolor Desf.
Rainbow ophrys

With the impressive, iridescent blue colour of the blazon and its characteristic purple colouring on the lower surface of the lip, this plant is easily recognised. Also characteristic is the little V-shaped groove which is created by the two swellings at the base of the trilobate, downy lip. The sepals are green and the petals are oblong, brownish-pink in colour. Found in phrygana, often beneath bushes.

Crete, Rhodes, Aegean, Sterea, Attica, Peloponnese | Up to 30cm ↑ |

| 1 | 2 | 3 | 4 | 5 | 6 | 7 | 8 | 9 | 10 | 11 | 12 |

Ophrys omegaifera H. Fleischm.
Ophrys omegaifera

The lip is brownish-red, downy, and three-lobed with a smooth blazon, lighter in colour, which is edged in white or blue in the manner of the Greek letter 'ω' (omega). The basal groove is missing from the strongly curved lip – this distinguishes it from O. fusca which often has the same blazon. The sepals are green and the petals have a russet-coloured, billowy edge.

◀ The endemic subspecies O. omegaifera ssp. *ba-silissa* is differentiated by its very large flowers with a lip which can reach to 3cm. Found in phrygana.

Crete, Rhodes, Aegean | Up to 50cm ↑ |

| 1 | 2 | 3 | 4 | 5 | 6 | 7 | 8 | 9 | 10 | 11 | 12 |

Ophrys phryganae J. & P. Devillers-Terschuren   ORCHIDACEAE
Phrygana ophrys

The lip is three-lobed and can reach up to 1.5cm. It is distinguished by the yellow border to its pattern, while in the centre it is brownish with a blazon that can take various metallic shades. The sepals are green and the petals small and yellowish-green. The downward turn of the lip at the base of the blazon is characteristic. The similar-looking *O. lutea* and *O. sicula* have larger and smaller lips respectively, which are unturned. A very frequently-occurring species, especially on the islands.

O. sicula

Distributed | 10-30cm ↑ | 🏔 ↓ | 1 | 2 | 3 | 4 | 5 | 6 | 7 | 8 | 9 | 10 | 11 | 12 |

Ophrys sphegodes Mill.   ORCHIDACEAE
Early spider orchid

A delicate plant which can reach a height of 50cm. The lip is brownish-red, ovate, and undivided with two little downy humps in place of the lateral lobes. The blazon resembles that of *O. spruneri*. The sepals and petals are green, the latter sometimes brownish.

Sterea, Attica, Peloponnese, Aegean, Crete | 10-50cm ↑ | 🏔 ↓ | 1 | 2 | 3 | 4 | 5 | 6 | 7 | 8 | 9 | 10 | 11 | 12 |

Ophrys spruneri NYMAN
Grecian spider orchid

ORCHIDACEAE

A very beautiful orchid with impressive colouring. The lip is clearly three-lobed, ovate - as are the smaller side lobes – and downy. The blazon has an intense metallic blue and light mauve device in the form of the letter 'H' which is sometimes interrupted in the middle. At the edge of the lip there is a small russet-colured protuberance pointing upwards. The sepals are pink, darker on the underside, and the petals are narrow, from red to green in colour. Relatively rare, found in phrygana and olive groves.

Distributed | Up to 40cm ↑ | 🔺 ⚓

| 1 | 2 | 3 | 4 | 5 | 6 | 7 | 8 | 9 | 10 | 11 | 12 |

Ophrys tenthredinifera WILLD.
Wasp ophrys, sawfly orchid

ORCHIDACEAE

Although a common species, *O. tenthredinifera* is one of the most beautiful orchids. The sepals are pink and the small petals the same colour. The lip is undivided, downy, yellow on the edges and brownish towards the centre, with two little humps on the shoulders and a small, yellow protuberance at the tip which is turned upwards. The blazon is smooth, brownish-red with a light coloured outline, orange at the base. Found in phrygana, open stony locations and thickets.

Sterea, Peloponnese, Aegean, Crete | 10-45cm ↑ | 🔺 ⚓

| 1 | 2 | 3 | 4 | 5 | 6 | 7 | 8 | 9 | 10 | 11 | 12 |

Orchis anatolica Boiss.
Anatolian orchid

A plant with a russet-coloured stem and grassy green leaves, dappled, and growing in a rosette. The flowers are pink to white with a large lip which has three spreading lobes. At the centre, which is light-coloured, there are two series of purple spots almost the whole length of the lip. Found in phrygana and stony locations.

Rhodes, Aegean, Crete | 15-40cm ↑ | ▲ ⬇

| 1 | 2 | 3 | 4 | 5 | 6 | 7 | 8 | 9 | 10 | 11 | 12 |

Orchis boryi Rchb.
Borys orchid

This orchid has the peculiarity that the upper flowers bloom first of all and thereafter the lower ones. It is dark reddish-violet or mauve in colour and the lip is light-coloured at the centre with irregular dark spots. The lip is almost semicircular, slightly divided into three lobes. The spur is of the same size as the ovary. The stem is russet-coloured at the flower-spike. Found in open meadow areas.

Peloponnese, Crete, Sterea, Aegean, Evvia | 20-30cm ↑ | ▲ ⬇

| 1 | 2 | 3 | 4 | 5 | 6 | 7 | 8 | 9 | 10 | 11 | 12 |

Orchis collina Banks & Sol.
Hill orchid

ORCHIDACEAE

One of the first orchids to flower, this is distinguished by its undivided lip and the short, sack-like spur. The sepals are brownish-green and the lip a variety of colours from green to pink, often light-coloured at the base. It is usually found in phrygana and dry meadows.

Crete, Rhodes, Aegean, Attica | 10-40cm ↑ | ▲ ↓

Orchis fragrans Pollini
Bug orchid

ORCHIDACEAE

The scent of this orchid is reminiscent of vanilla. It is a delicate, greenish-pink plant with a dense inflorescence. The sepals and the two petals form a sharply-peaked dome. The lip is three-lobed, the middle lobe longer, with strong red spotting at the centre. The spur is relatively short with a slight downwards inclination. Found in phrygana and meadows where there is dampness.

◄ *O. coriophora* is found in central mainland Greece and resembles *O. fragrans*, with the difference that it has darker-coloured flowers and a rank aroma.

Distributed | 10-30cm ↑ | ▲ ↓

Orchis italica Poir.

ORCHIDACEAE

Wavy-leaved monkey orchid,

This is a widely occurring plant with a dense spike that is spherical, ovoid or pyramid-shaped, and has wavy leaves, often with dark spots. The flowers are polymorphic, pink to white with a three-lobed lip, and the middle lobe is also trilobate. The sepals and petals form a dome with the result that the whole appearance of the flower resembles that of a little man with a phallus. It was perhaps for this reason that the ancient Greeks called it 'satyrion', since it broadly resembled a satyr in appearance. The spur is relatively short, and turned downwards. The plant is often found in dense populations.

Distributed | 20-40cm ↑ | ▲ ⚓

| 1 | 2 | 3 | 4 | 5 | 6 | 7 | 8 | 9 | 10 | 11 | 12 |

Orchis lactea POIR.
Milky orchid

ORCHIDACEAE

A beautiful orchid which has white or rose-pink flowers with pink stippling. The lip is three-lobed with the middle lobe larger, wavy at the edges, and undivided. The sepals are greenish at the base and form a closed dome together with the petals. The spur is strong, and turned downwards. Found in phrygana and grassy meadows.

◀ *Orchis lactea* x *Orchis tridentata*

Distributed | 10-20cm ↑ | ▲ ↓

| 1 | 2 | 3 | 4 | 5 | 6 | 7 | 8 | 9 | 10 | 11 | 12 |

Orchis laxiflora LAM.
Jersey or Lax-flowered orchid

ORCHIDACEAE

A tall plant with a loose inflorescence. The leaves are narrow and ridged. The flowers are usually a light pink, almost white at the centre. The lip is trilobate with the middle lobe smaller than the lateral lobes, the latter hanging downwards. It prefers damp localities and marshes. The same biotopes are also chosen by *O. palustris*, which is similar, but relatively larger, lighter in colour, and has horizontal lateral lobes.

Distributed | 30-60m ↑ | ▲ ↓

| 1 | 2 | 3 | 4 | 5 | 6 | 7 | 8 | 9 | 10 | 11 | 12 |

Orchis mascula L.
ORCHIDACEAE
Early purple orchid

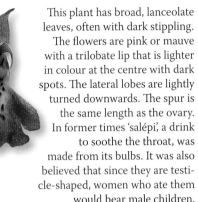

This plant has broad, lanceolate leaves, often with dark stippling. The flowers are pink or mauve with a trilobate lip that is lighter in colour at the centre with dark spots. The lateral lobes are lightly turned downwards. The spur is the same length as the ovary. In former times 'salépi', a drink to soothe the throat, was made from its bulbs. It was also believed that since they are testicle-shaped, women who ate them would bear male children.

Epirus, Samos | 10-50cm ↑ |

| 1 | 2 | 3 | 4 | 5 | 6 | 7 | 8 | 9 | 10 | 11 | 12 |

Orchis papilionacea L.
ORCHIDACEAE
Butterfly orchid

The plant has fluted, lanceolate leaves without spotting. The flowers are butterfly-shaped with sepals and petals that are darker than the lip and have deep red veining. The bracts are dark-coloured, longer than the ovary. The lip is light-coloured with pink lines and stippling, undivided, and lightly undulating at the edges. The flower-heads are relatively dense but contain few flowers. Found in phrygana and open, dry locations.

◀ *Orchis papilionacea* x
Orchis tridentata

Distributed | 20-40cm ↑ |

| 1 | 2 | 3 | 4 | 5 | 6 | 7 | 8 | 9 | 10 | 11 | 12 |

Orchis pauciflora TEN.
Sparsely-flowering orchid

A relatively small plant with fluted, lanceolate leaves without stippling. The flowers are whitish-yellow, with an almost yellow lip, trilobate, irregularly toothed with dark red, irregular flecks and slight green shading at the centre. The spur is long, larger than the ovary. Found in phrygana in rocky locations.

Distributed | 10-30cm ↑ | 1 2 3 4 5 6 7 8 9 10 11 12

Orchis provincialis BALB.   ORCHIDACEAE
Provence orchid

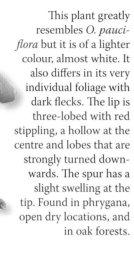

This plant greatly resembles *O. pauci-flora* but it is of a lighter colour, almost white. It also differs in its very individual foliage with dark flecks. The lip is three-lobed with red stippling, a hollow at the centre and lobes that are strongly turned downwards. The spur has a slight swelling at the tip. Found in phrygana, open dry locations, and in oak forests.

Distributed | Up to 30cm ↑ | ▲ ↧   1 2 3 4 5 6 7 8 9 10 11 12

Orchis quadripunctata CIRILLO EX TEN.   ORCHIDACEAE
Orchis quadripunctata

This beautiful plant, usually short with few flowers, has a dark red stem and leaves with dark flecks. The flowers range from pink to white with outspread sepals and a very thin, long spur. The lip is three-lobed, lighter coloured at the base, and normally bears four spots, a characteristic which has given it its name. Found in stony locations.

Distributed | 5-40cm ↑ | ▲ ↧   1 2 3 4 5 6 7 8 9 10 11 12

Orchis simia L.AM.
Monkey orchid

ORCHIDACEAE

A very robust orchid, generally resembling *O. italica* with which it hybridizes. The leaves are in a rosette, and without undulations. The flower is pink, and white in the centre. The sepals and petals form a dome which looks like a head, while the central lip is three-lobed with the middle lobe bilobate with a pointed-tipped little 'tail' at the centre. The general appearance of the flower vividly recalls that of a monkey – hence the name. Relatively rare, it prefers phyrgana thickets.

Orchis simia x
Orchis italica

Distributed | 10-40cm ↑ |

Orchis sitiaca (Renz) Delforge

ORCHIDACEAE

Orchis sitiaca

This plant resembles *O. anatolica*, but differs in the very particular appearance of the silver-green leaves, which have only few or no spots, and in the much later flowering-time. The lobes of the lip are strongly turned downwards. Another particular characteristic is constituted by the green nerves on the inside of the sepals. Endemic to the mountains of Crete.

Crete | 15-25cm ↑ | 🏔 ⚱

| 1 | 2 | 3 | 4 | 5 | 6 | 7 | 8 | 9 | 10 | 11 | 12 |

Orchis tridentata Scop.

ORCHIDACEAE

Three-toothed orchid

This resembles *O. lactea* but differs in that the sepals do not completely close the dome and the tips of them form three teeth, a characteristic which gives the plant its name. The lip is three-lobed with the middle lobe larger, also divided with a little protuberance at the centre. All of the tips of the lobes are pointed. Found in bushy phrygana thickets.

Distributed | 20-40cm ↑ | 🏔 ⚱ ◆

| 1 | 2 | 3 | 4 | 5 | 6 | 7 | 8 | 9 | 10 | 11 | 12 |

Serapias cordigera L.
Heart-flowered serapias

The serapies do not have the impressive colouring and forms of the other orchids, since they are all more or less of the same brownish-violet colour and form. The result is that their identification is often difficult. S. cordigera is the rarest among them and has a large, reddish-pink heart-shaped lip which differentiates it. A particular characteristic is also constituted by the dark spots at the base of the stem and leaves. Found in phrygana and in low thickets.

Distributed | 20-40cm ↑ | ▲ ⚓ | 1 | 2 | 3 | 4' | 5 | 6 | 7 | 8 | 9 | 10 | 11 | 12 |

Serapias lingua L.
Tongue serapias, tongue orchid

This is the smallest of the serapies and easily differentiated by its tongue-like lip, a characteristic which gives the plant its name. The swellings present in other varieties at the base of the lip are absent in S. lingua, while another characteristic is the black fleck located there. The bracts are of the same length as the flowers which are usually of a violet or white colour. Found in phrygana, thickets, and grassy meadows, and has a preference for damp locations.

Distributed | 15-30cm ↑ | ▲ ⚓ | 1 | 2 | 3 | 4 | 5 | 6 | 7 | 8 | 9 | 10 | 11 | 12 |

Serapias orientalis (GREUTER) H. BAUMANN & KÜNKELE   ORCHIDACEAE
Eastern serapias

This is a relatively small plant with a very long pointed lip which is often turned backwards. The flowers are usually concentrated in a terminal, rather compact inflorescence. The two dark lateral lobes of the lip which protrude clearly from the sheath are characteristic. Found in meadows and pine forests with a preference for damp soil.

Crete, Rhodes, Aegean | Up to 30cm ↑ | 🏔 ⚓

| 1 | 2 | 3 | 4 | 5 | 6 | 7 | 8 | 9 | 10 | 11 | 12 |

Spiranthes spiralis KOCH.   ORCHIDACEAE
Autumn Lady's Tresses

This tiny, relatively rare orchid is the only one which flowers in autumn. The leaves are concentrated in a rosette at the base of the plant and develop in spring. The inflorescence with the little white flowers has a characteristic spiral arrangement. Found in phrygana, thickets, pine forests and olive groves.

Distributed | Up to 30cm ↑ | 🏔 ⚓

| 1 | 2 | 3 | 4 | 5 | 6 | 7 | 8 | 9 | 10 | 11 | 12 |

BIBLIOGRAPHY

Α. Άλκιμος, *Μακεδονική γη, εικόνες από την χλωρίδα και την πανίδα*, Αθήνα 1997

Α. Άλκιμος, *Οι ορχιδέες της Ελλάδας*, Αθήνα 1988

Θ. Αραμπατζή, *Αγριολούλουδα του παρθένου δάσους Δράμας*, Δράμα 1997

Θ. Αραμπατζή, *Θάμνοι και δέντρα στην Ελλάδα*, Δράμα 2001

Ε. Βάθης, *Τα φυτά του πάρκου της Αρχαίας Αγοράς*, Αθήνα 2002

M. Blamey, C. Grey-Wilson, *Wild Flowers of the Mediterranean*

D. Burnie, *Wildflowers of the Mediterranean*

Π. Γενναδίου, *Φυτολογικό Λεξικό*, Αθήναι 1914

N. Goulandris, C. Goulimis, *Wild Flowers of Greece*, Athens 1968

A. Huxley, *Flowers in Greece, an outline of the flora*, London 1972

R. Jahn, P. Schönfelder, *Excursionsflora für Kreta*, Stuttgart 1995

Δ. Καββαδα, *Εικονογραφημένον Βοτανικόν-Φυτολογικόν Λεξικόν*, Αθήναι

Η. Καϊναδάς, Ν. Μάργαρης, Μ. Θεοδωρακάκης, *Τα αγριολούλουδα της Αθήνας*, Αθήνα 1997

H. & G. Kretzschmar, W Eccarius, *Ορχιδέες, Κρήτη και Δωδεκάνησα*, Ρέθυμνο 2004

Έ. Μπάουμαν, *Η Ελληνική χλωρίδα στο μύθο, στην τέχνη στη λογοτεχνία*, Αθήνα 1984

Β. Παπιομύτογλου, *Σαμαριά, το Φαράγγι και τα Λευκά Όρη*, Ρέθυμνο 2006

O. Polunin, A. Huxley, *Flowers of the Mediterranean*, London 1987

O. Polunin, *Flowers of Greece and the Balkans*, Oxford 1987

A. Strid, *Mountain flora of Greece*, Vol. 1, Cambridge 1986

A. Strid, Kit Tan, *Mountain flora of Greece*, Vol. 2, Edinburg 1991

A. Strid, *Wild flowers of mount Olympus*, Αθήνα 1980

Γ. Σφήκα, *Αγριολούλουδα της Ελλάδας*, Αθήνα

Γ. Σφήκα, *Αγριολούλουδα της Κρήτης*, Αθήνα

Γ. Σφήκα, *Οι βοτανικοί παράδεισοι της Ελλάδας*, Αθήνα 2001

Kit Tan, G. Iatrou, *Endemic plants of Greece, the Peloponnese*, Copenhagen 2001

The Red Data Book of Rare and Threatened plants of Greece, 1995

N. J. Turland, L. Chilton, J. R. Press *Flora of the Cretan area*, London 1993

J. Zaffran, *Contributions a la flore et a la vegetation de la Crete*, Aix en Provence 1990